PRACTICAL PEST CONTROL
IN THE COUNTRYSIDE

PRACTICAL PEST CONTROL
IN THE COUNTRYSIDE

George Hogg

THE BOYDELL PRESS

First published 1986 by The Boydell Press
an imprint of Boydell & Brewer Ltd
PO Box 9, Woodbridge, Suffolk IP12 3DF and
51 Washington Street, Dover, New Hampshire 03820, USA

ISBN 0 85115 436 0

British Library Cataloguing in Publication Data available

Hogg, George, 1953–
Practical pest control.
1. Pests——Control——Great Britain
I. Title
632.6'0941   SB950.3.G7

ISBN 0-85115-436-0

Library of Congress Cataloguing in Publication Data applied for

Hogg, George, 1953–
Practical pest control.

1. Pests—Control—Great Britain.   I. Title.
SB950.3.G7H64   1986   628.9'6'0941   85-29000
ISBN 0-85115-436-0

Printed in Great Britain by
St Edmundsbury Press, Bury St Edmunds, Suffolk

Contents

Introduction

Welcome, dear reader: those who know me through articles 'from Pester's Pen' in Shooting News and those who have picked up this book due to a general interest in country topics, a specific interest in rural pest control problems, or sheer curiosity as to just what the pesters profession is all about!

In brief this is a book about those British wild animals which from time to time require some sort of management to prevent damage, disease or distress to people, livestock, crops, rural property and so on. I am a country pest control specialist and this book concerns the place of traditional methods in modern commercial pest control. It is unfortunately true that big business chemical pest control has produced a reliance upon science and has led to an erosion of the many skills of the country verminman. Through this book I hope to redress the balance a little. I hope to persuade some modern pest controllers to develop some of the traditional old skills. Conversely I hope to promote among country verminmen an interest in the new chemical methods. While doing so I also hope to present the casual reader with a fascinating insight into the old methods of the country 'catcher, his dogs, ferrets and his methods which, old or not, should be regarded as being reinforced by chemical methods – certainly not replaced by them. At present a rural customer such as a large farm or estate has the greatest difficulty in finding a pester: a modern firm from the nearest town will be employed to set rodenticide baits throughout the farm buildings for the rats and mice. A verminman from the village will be engaged on rabbit control in the woods and rough corners. The local mole contractor will visit occasionally to straighten out the fields. A sportsman, when he can spare the time, will oblige by trying to protect crops and forestry from pigeons, hares and deer. The gamekeeper, who increasingly today is part time or even amateur, will take care of foxes, stoats, mink and other killers of poultry, livestock and game. From the customer's viewpoint the ideal would be a verminman proficient in all the above tasks. The vocation of such a man is a natural one. He is part and parcel of nature, a participant rather than a spectator. His life is of the sort so envied in today's worried world. His is the Verminman's Vocation; the Pester's Profession.

PART ONE

1

The Pests

Ask the layman what a pest is. There is every chance he will reply with a short list of common pest species such as rabbit, rat, mouse, flea etc. To tell the truth, some pest controllers might reply the same way. Ask an animal lover, particularly an animal rights campaigner, and you'll hear that 'Man is the only pest on earth' – a statement of partial truth.

Ask me and I'll answer you thus. An animal becomes a pest because of where, not what it is. It is unfair to say that any particular species is a pest. The rural fox is killed on sight for the threat his over-population presents to lambs, poultry, game and ground nesting wildlife. Urban foxes on the other hand are seen by humans far more often than their country cousins: humans moreover whose opportunities of observing wildlife are severely limited. Thus they give a great deal of pleasure to a great many people. In towns, there's very little damage foxes can do: lambs, poultry, game and wildlife are a bit thin on the ground where man abounds. So we have one species which is pest in the woods and fields but not in our towns and gardens.

This example of foxes is a reversal of the general rule, because those which have come in from their proper place are no problem whereas those which remain where they should be require control as pests. Normally animals only become pests when their territories infringe on our own and they interfere with our stock, crops, health and home, bringing with them the 'three D's' – Disease, Damage and Distress – which are our classic reasons for applying control and labelling an animal a 'pest'.

A tiny bitch weasel on the moors may live a comparatively crime free life. But let her enter the nearest poultry hatchery and just watch how swiftly the verminman is summoned. For this reason 'control' need not necessarily mean the death sentence. Transportation to a more suitable site is often enough to rectify the matter, particularly when dealing with an uncommon species. However, beware of the law regarding the 'spreading' of pests.

Rules regarding movement of native species and introduction of alien species are scattered throughout various statutes e.g. the various Pest and Agricultural Acts, Wildlife & Countryside Act etc. etc. Normally when a species becomes legally protected some provision is made for removal or control of rogue offenders, as in the Badgers Act 1973.

Alternatives

Fortunately, as the best pesters are also naturalists, there is, or should be, some reluctance to kill uncommon species where there exists alternative solutions such as proofing, repelling, dispersal or denial of necessities such as the food supply, water source or shelter, thereby forcing the problem to go away of its' own accord.

Be you customer or verminman, always consider the alternatives before declaring war. Weeds are only wild flowers in the wrong place. Pests are only wild animals in the wrong place. With so many environmental pressures upon wildlife these days, we cannot assume the right to cut them down like so many weeds. Unlike weeds, those which must be cut down should be cut down as cleanly and humanely as possible. It would be gratifying to think that this modest book might prevent any undue suffering caused through unknowledgeable attempts at pest control.

2

The Past and Present

In the recent past verminmen had it all their own way. There were no big pest control companies or marvel cures of the type used by today's competitors. For that reason and due to our own dirty habits, rats, mice and other 'commercial pests' were far more numerous than now. Every verminman had his dogs, ferrets, traps and a few old and highly dangerous natural poisons such as red squills. Only within living memory did the use of this plant extract die out. Such instant poisons had the disadvantage of letting rats see their fellows killed. This, and the fact that sub-lethal doses only caused illness, produced the problem of 'bait-shy' rodents. The same shyness results when traps alone are used to clear large infestations of rats. All the reckless ones get caught, only the cautious ones survive; result – 'trap shy' rats.

Of course, there were specialists in all departments of rural pest control. Rabbit trapping alone was an industry of national importance. Mole trappers were to be found in every parish. Ratcatchers found constant employment and couldn't fail to make impressive catches during such an infested era. Every estate employed numerous gamekeepers, and vermin was killed ruthlessly, in such a way that the polecat and some birds of prey have never fully recovered to this day. Mind you, polecats, raptors and others aren't now considered pests. Times have changed. And how times have changed! Myxomatosis saw a massive decline in rabbits and the near extinction of full-time rabbit catchers. Agricultural 'improvements' have done away with much of the old mole-riddled fieldscape. Highly effective rodenticides have reduced the nation's rat and mouse population to a fraction of their former status. The passing of the great estates has led to one gamekeeper being employed where once there were twenty.

All in all, there has come a situation wherein most country 'catchers can no longer afford to specialise. To find enough work they must be jacks of all trades: though this restricts the crafts of the verminman, it is very much to the benefit of the customer who can now call on one familiar figure, whatever the pest problem.

Those long established industries of rabbiters, ratters, molecatchers and game preservers have not entirely died out, of course. Rather they have been condensed. Now the old skills survive in a reduced number of non-specialists, beneficiaries of a wealth of experience and expertise from days and men gone by.

Some old methods have been outlawed along the way, and rightly so. Those were hard times all round, and sentiment fell mainly on stony ground. No right-thinking person will mourn the passing of the toothed gin trap, irrespective of its undoubted efficiency. The widespread trade in rabbit meat, and skins for the fashionable felt top hats of the day, revolved wholly around the use of this leg biting device.

Other improvements are seen in our enlightened attitude towards 'pests'. No longer is wildlife slain out of hand with little consideration of the effect on our natural heritage. Though verminmen were far more numerous in the past, the society they lived in was harder, less educated and far more liable to take the countryside for granted. Their skills were undeniable but some of their ethics were rather questionable. Yet it has to be said that the Victorians and Edwardians have a far superior track record in their care and management of the countryside than we have in the 'conservation' minded eighties. We are never done talking about conservation, but only a few ever do anything about it.

Ancient profession or not, the verminman's vocation is very much a trade of today and tomorrow. It is alive and well and has much to teach us about practical management of the countryside as opposed to the wishy-washy protectionism preached, yet poorly practiced, by some conservationists today.

Science

Science in the early twentieth century attempted to replace the old natural pesticides, most of which were plant extracts. It did so in a manner typical of a time when nations were prepared to use nerve gas on soldiers let alone 'vermin'. The new poisons, 'acute' or single dose, gave no hope for any innocent dog, cat or farm stock which chanced upon the bait. These lethal chemicals in the hands of unscientific countrymen were a bit of a liability, to say the least. Pests, particularly rodents, did suffer a set back and for the first time there really was an element of 'control' but not without risk. Then came the dawn of the 'chronic' or multi-dose rodenticides, particularly 'Warfarin'. This new breed of rodenticide was safer to the user, the customer, wildlife and domestic animals. Chronic poisons did not produce bait shy survivors among the treated rodents. They worked by causing a build-up of poison in the rodents over several days. Until their coming it was necessary for verminmen to be naturalists/hunters; but now change was in the offing. The world of commerce was quick to realise that here was an opening. Now

4

anyone could become a pest controller and firms quickly came into being specialising in the application of modern rodenticides and insecticides. Salesmen were hired to tour town and country signing up customers on contracts for X number of visits per year. At each visit a 'serviceman' would survey the premises, shop, factory, hospital, farm buildings and so on, detect any insect or rodent problem, and spray or bait with the appropriate chemical. Results were impressive. Society was becoming sophisticated and was eager to embrace this scientific image. Things began to look grim for the local verminman, his dog and ferrets!

Such is the position today, with two very different types of worker, the pest controller and the verminman. The first (very much in the majority) tends to be part of a firm, the latter an individual. The one tends to specialise in 'commercial' pests, i.e. rats, mice, certain insects and town pigeons. The other takes care of rats, mice, seldom if ever insects, and a long list of non-commercial pests including foxes, stoats, mink, hooded and carrion crows, grey squirrels, rabbits and moles. The first, in many cases, has never heard of the second! Somewhere between the chemical-orientated operators and the traditional verminers, there exists a third type. These are the men whose skills embrace the methods and quarry lists of both old and new schools. They are the ones I consider complete pest controllers, treating all problems from fleas to foxes. They are my type of 'catcher and I sincerely hope this book persuades any readers who might encounter future pest problems to ensure the man they call in is such an all rounder.

3

Tools of the Trade

Enough has already been said about commercial, big business pest control. There are more than enough books on that subject already. Now there is this one which focuses on the forgotten fringe of pest control, the part big firms patronisingly look upon as the history of pest control. No doubt they won't like to be reminded in print of the many methods they don't use and the many pests they don't control. Having said all that I must top this list of tools of the trade with the main tool of the commercial trade – pesticides. There can be no doubt that poisons, especially for rats and mice, are easily the most useful tool of the country verminman as well as his town counterpart. But maybe too much is known about pesticides already. Nothing like enough is known of the non-chemical methods so it's on with the list and from this point I promise no further reference to anything other than country topics.

All methods listed in this chapter will be looked into more fully later on; their inclusion here is only by way of an appetite-whetter and scene-setter.

Dogs

Verminmen are easily recognised. They are invariably shadowed by at least one vermin dog. You won't see many vermin dogs at Crufts or around the town park, so let me describe them for you. They are large, small, rough and smooth coated, long-legged, short-legged, ugly, pretty or pretty ugly. They come in all shapes and sizes, no two look alike; but all that is on the outside. Unlike those who breed pedigree dogs, verminmen only bother about the inside of their dogs. Brains, ability, instinct, and above all usefulness are the qualities they are bred for. Looks are rarely considered in their making. For that reason verminmen are to be seen with some weird canine partners in tow. I agree vermin dogs look like nothing on earth, until they are seen working: then nothing on earth looks like a vermin dog!

Ferrets

Ferrets, on the other hand, don't vary much. Reared properly, they are quiet, calm pets. Put them among rats or rabbits, however, and their polecat ancestors come to the fore. The speed with which their burrowing foes forsake the warrens tells us of the ferocity of the unseen attack below. Yet when the last rat or rabbit has fled or been killed, out comes ferret to be picked up as easily as any kitten. What Jekyll and Hyde animals they are! In time a working relationship develops, and the teamwork between pester, dog and ferrets has to be seen to be believed.

Traps

Traps used by the modern pester are not the cruel old leg-pulling toothed monstrosities the word brings to mind. Modern traps are designed to do one of two things: catch alive and unharmed, as do the wide variety of cage traps in use; or kill cleanly and instantaneously, as do the approved humane spring traps on the market. The old image of trappers as uncaring barbarians couldn't be further from the truth: the better the naturalist the better the trapper.

Snares

Snares, which laymen often confuse with traps, are no more than free running wire nooses positioned over animal runs to catch around the neck. If the animal is travelling at speed it may be killed outright. If not, it quickly realises that to pull is to tighten the noose. Then it will squat down and remain still until the pester arrives to despatch it.

Nets

Nets are mainly used when it is known where the quarry lies and, more importantly which way escape will be made upon being disturbed. Nets can then be placed over burrow mouths, fieldgates, woodland rides, drain pipes and such like. Man, dog, or ferret then drives the quarry into the nets. You think that nothing could be simpler? The making and using of nets is an art in itself.

1 Spotlight & spillproof battery (12v) used for "lamping" rabbits and foxes.

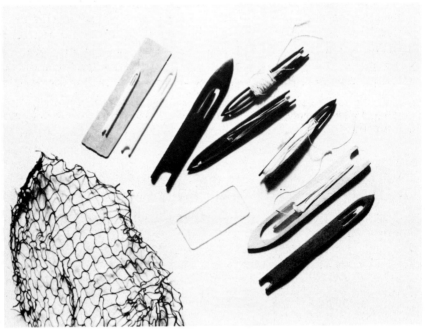

2 Net making materials.

Guns

Shotguns and rifles are the two favoured firearms of the pester. Shotguns naturally are best for moving targets. Rifles are preferred when stalking stationary or slow moving prey which is unaware of the gunner's presence. Of course, it isn't practical to carry both. Personally I've always favoured the rifle as the one to sling over my back or to lie handy in the back of the van.

Skills

There is one other thing the complete verminman must be equipped with. Unlike the tools already listed this commodity is not one which can be bought. I refer to the pesters' skills as a naturalist/hunter - an ability to read the countryside, tracks, trails and signs; an understanding, knowledge and sympathy for all that goes on around him; a feeling of being a participant in nature rather than a spectator. It is the attitude which separates practical countrymen from mere 'animal lovers'.

It may come as a surprise to some protectionists to hear that a man may be both naturalist and hunter. If we humans must kill a certain number of animals in the name of pest control, is it not better if the pester is also a naturalist? His sympathy will ensure there is no cruelty. Where other remedies are available he will avoid killing. In cases where 'culling' is necessary he will ensure he chooses from his wide range of methods the quickest, cleanest and most humane way applicable in the circumstances. Of all the tools of the trade this one may be the most important.

Now, having glimpsed all the pieces of the puzzle, let's see how the jigsaw fits together ...

4

Pesticides

Articles 'From Pester's Pen' in *Shooting News* often result in readers' replies to the magazine or to me personally. Most seek advice, but I'm always keen to hear others' opinions. One verminman, an ex-gamekeeper from Gloucestershire crossed swords with me on the issue of pesticides. He was dead against their use in any circumstances. His methods included all those listed in the previous chapter but not 'dreaded poisons'. As stated earlier, there are those who use only pesticides and those who use everything but pesticides. RJP was a clear example of the latter. He claimed to make a 'decent living without resorting to poisoning' and I have no doubt he does: there are obviously customers in his district who appreciate the traditional touch. Equally there will be potential customers who favour the scientific approach: and here is custom he is missing out on. Having said that I hope to persuade some such men to encompass a working knowledge of pesticides among their skills, I also recognise that pesticides could present a danger in the hands of some dyed-in-the-wool traditionalists (just as dogs, traps, snares and ferrets could present a danger in the hands of some completely unnatural urban pesters). Somewhere between these two extremes, however, we may make a few converts.

There are, of course, laws about how pesticides should be used. The habitat of the verminman is one shared by nosey farm dogs, free-range poultry, rummaging sheep, foraging goats and all sorts of animals likely to eat any tasty morsel they happen across. Pesticides have improved greatly as regards safety over the years; most now require several feeds to kill. No poison is 'safe', however, and great care must be taken to protect the bait from all 'non-target' species. Rat poison by the bucketful is set out by the typical pester each winter, when rats come into farm buildings. It should, however, be impossible to see any poison during a walk through the buildings. Pipes, boards, old doors, corrugated iron sheets and all manner of farm yard clutter can be pressed into providing 'bait points' against external and internal walls. Rats always run along wall bottoms and prefer to feed in the security and darkness of such cover. There is a knack in tossing together the above junk in such a way as to encourage rats and yet repel dogs, livestock and ever-inquisitive sparrows. Most of the poisons handled by pesters are used in this way for rats and mice.

Only a few other animals require chemical methods. Of these the main one is the mole. Moles always were prime candidates for poison treatments. Planting mole traps over several fields and subsequently inspecting them takes far more time and effort than the placing of poisoned earthworms in their underground burrows. Only strychnine should be used for moles. More important, strychnine may not be used above ground for any other animal or even below ground in any other type of burrow. Unlike rodent baits there is no such thing as precautionary bait for moles, i.e. a bait set in a cleared area to prevent any reinfestation. For this reason mole traps still have a place, particularly on land near woodland. Clearing moles from such ground tends to make way for others within a very short time. A well-sited trap on sentry duty will stop any counter-attack.

Grey squirrels may also be baited but, as in all cases, there are safety measures. In the open woodland habitat where this species is inclined to cause damage, it is very difficult to set up a bait which only squirrels will have access to. There are special bait hoppers on the market for this purpose. Where both red and grey squirrels occur it can be a problem clearing the greys and leaving the reds. On such jobs, poisons are of course not suitable.

For most other pests the use of poison baits is either illegal or strictly regulated by law. Poison may not be used at all to kill birds. Birds may only be temporarily narcotised by a mild stupefying bait which enables them to be caught by hand and humanely destroyed. This can only be done under licence from the Ministry of Agriculture and it is very rare for licences to be granted for any birds other than feral pigeons and house sparrows.

Other than baits intended for consumption by pests, there are one or two other chemical methods. Rodent Contact Powder is a highly static dust which is inserted into dead spaces such as wall cavities where rodents are known to be active. As the rat or mouse scurries across the dust, its paws and underfur become thinly coated in the stuff. Unknowingly the creature licks this whilst grooming and preening (activities which rodents have a compulsion for). Because far less poison is taken this way, as opposed to an edible bait, contact poisons tend to contain a far higher percentage of 'active ingredient' – sometimes as much as 50 per cent. When you consider most baits contain far less than 1 per cent poison, it goes without saying that contact dusts should be treated with the utmost care.

Gassing is a treatment used for rats, rabbits and foxes. Actually the preparation comes in powder or tablet form. When sealed in a burrow it reacts with the soil's moisture to give off a highly poisonous gas, usually cyanide. Gassing is possibly today's main method of rabbit control. I know of rabbit control specialists who use nothing else. As in all pest control matters, no one method is infallible. Effective gassing requires the correct soil type to contain the fumes, and for this reason it is sometimes a lethal method and sometimes a disappointment.

Being a country pest controller who occasionally works in town and is often asked about the job by 'suburbanites' I marvel at the way some modern folk think. Apparently society in its new-found sophistication has been brain-washed into accepting as 'humane' anything produced by the 'boffins', be it gas, contact dust, strychnine or whatever. Mention that part of your dog's work involves killing things, and they throw up their hands in horror! Nature must have it all wrong! Once on a commercial pest control course, a lecturer stated a pesticide was 'anything which killed pests'. He then posed the question 'which is the fastest acting rodenticide?' After much deliberation my fellow students came up with the reply 'zinc phosphide' which answer the lecturer accepted. Asking how long it took to act, I received the reply 'ten seconds'. There was great hilarity when I pointed out that my dog back home must be the 'fastest acting rodenticide' as she only took two seconds! I enjoy a laugh but the joke served to point out that craft can often better chemistry and dogs are far less dangerous than zinc phosphide!

5

The Verminman's Dog

Forget the Giant Panda, Mr Attenborough: the vermin dog is in far more need of your protection!

For the life of me, I cannot see how this job can be done properly without a good dog. Yet I have actually met pest controllers who have assumed the dog in my van is there to keep me company – little do they realise she may know more of the job than they do!

What then are the duties of this dog? First and foremost is the ability to find and indicate the exact spot where pests are hiding. This a trained dog can do within inches, frequently in places where discovery would have been impossible otherwise, such as in wall cavities, drains, burrows, farm machinery, etc. On jobs where, for instance, a single rat has been reported in extensive premises, a dog can turn a week's work into an hour's. Secondly, and of very secondary importance, a vermin dog must be able to catch, kill and, when required, retrieve. All this it must do under the strict control of the handler. It is up to the individual verminman how many dogs he should keep at one time. Personally I prefer to use only one. My reasons are simple. Appearing at a new job with a van load of dogs is hardly likely to help your image in the eyes of the customer, particularly if he is a farmer or estate factor with responsibility for livestock and game in the area. Remember there are circumstances where dogs can be classed as pests in the country. The person you are meeting has quite possibly had occasion to shoot several dogs in his lifetime! He will quite rightly treat your dogs with great suspicion and will require to be convinced of their steadiness to stock and usefulness with vermin before he agrees to their use.

A single dog, especially a small single dog, quickly becomes a firm favourite with the customers. Countrymen are always appreciative of a handy dog, be it sheepdog, cattledog, gundog, vermindog or whatever. I remember arriving at a farm in a neighbouring county. I was in the tricky situation of taking over from the farm's local and well-liked verminman who had recently left the profession. Here I was, a lanky, red-bearded stranger with a scruffy little grey dog. Not an imposing sight, I suppose, especially as my predecessor had not seen fit to use dogs. Fortunately the farm manager and a couple of workers were just about to tidy up a shed full of loose straw which was known to contain numerous rats. He suggested I return in a few days to poison the place as 'the rats will have scattered about the steading'. Instead I offered to help with the baling, and he was soon to discover my generosity had a motive. As the lads forked the straw into the baler I stood behind extracting the bales and building them into a wall around the scene of operations. By the time they were getting to the last of the straw (and the first of the rats) my wall was complete and all rat escape routes were blocked. Within an hour of arriving we were leaving. Each and every rat lay dead within the wall. The stranger and his weird looking dog had taken on a completely different image in the eyes of the farm staff. Much later when Paul, the manager, had become a friend, he admitted he had been converted within that hour to understanding the need for the verminman's dog.

But enough of killing: show me the pest controller who can sniff out a solitary rat in a farm steading full of cattle, sheep and hens! This is where dogs are at their most useful. Today's control methods are so effective the pester can often find himself in search of just one mouse, rat, rabbit, stoat or whatever. I once called at a hotel moments after the owner had seen a rat move between the rubbish bins. There was no way it could come out without being seen but he had searched high and low before I joined him. Together we moved everything in that little cluster of bins and bags but were totally bamboozled by the complete disappearance of the rat. The stuff was all against a rather loosely constructed old wall several feet high. We knew the rat hadn't climbed it and no holes could be found in the mortar at ground level. 'Do you mind if I try my dog?' She was fetched from the van and made complete amateurs of the hotelier and I by going straight to a tiny hole three feet up in the wall and marking strongly. She had found in seconds the rat which had evaded two men for ten minutes. Hundreds of similar examples could be cited to show the reason why this pester believes the verminman's vocation cannot be carried out by the verminman alone.

As I stated, I prefer just one dog at a time. I have had four at once, but found each got only a quarter of the training and work experience I could give to one. Those who use dogs in plural have the advantage of being able to use various specialists rather than one general purpose all-rounder. A terrier might be kept for ratting and foxing, a whippet for rabbiting and a labrador for shooting. The one-dog-man must find a canine partner capable of combining the jobs of all three. My choice is the lurcher.

Most of my dog work is against rat and rabbit, plus a certain amount of feral pigeon shooting. For this I use at present a 3/4 whippet – 1/4 Bedlington terrier. Never let anyone tell you the lurcher is a mongrel. Far from it: he is a carefully selected blend of canine ingredients, the particular recipe used depending upon the type of work he is being created for. Unlike other breeds, lurchers vary enormously from dog to dog and job to job. All they have in common is an abundant supply of greyhound or whippet blood –

3 Whippet/Bedlington "Heading" a rabbit "Running Cunning" only comes with long experience.

4 Snow pebbles on a Bedlington lurcher.

5 *Vermindog stalking rabbits.*

6 *Marking a rat beneath an old barrow. The dog won't move a whisker until the barrow is moved or a ferret slipped under to bolt the rat.*

between half and three quarters. The other parts of the mixture can be any breed which has not yet had its working instinct diluted by the showing fraternity. Working border and bearded collies are favourites, as are some of the working terrier breeds. There are many other crosses in use by lurcher breeders today, but some are chosen purely for shape with never a thought given to working instinct. Handsome is as handsome does, however, and it does not do to question any lurcher's breeding until it has been seen at work. Usefulness is all that matters. It may resemble a cross between a bunch of keys, a coconut doormat and a half melted welly! If it does the job and gets results it earns the title 'lurcher' and holds for me far more value than the annual Crufts Champion.

Be warned, however, there is a certain suspicion of the lurcher in many quarters, which is hardly surprising, considering his long association with the poaching fraternity: an alliance which persists to this day. For this reason I like a very small lurcher, her running dog lines camouflaged by a heavy coat, enabling her to be passed off as 'just a wee terrier for the rats'.

'Wee terrier for the rats' – the understatement of all time. Training a dog for this life is no overnight task. Training starts at seven weeks, work starts at seven months but I look upon five years as the point when training and practical experience finally produce an expert dog. At that stage there is little need to issue orders or commands at all. Just a discreet point, nod, whisper, whistle, hiss or even a movement of the eyebrows is enough. The dog knows the ropes as well as the pester: dog and man are at one with each other and with the job.

Five years may seem a long apprenticeship, but consider the vagaries of this schooling. The dog should kill and drop rats in an instant, ready for the next one. She should catch and retrieve rabbits alive to hand without as much as a bruise. During shooting she should watch pigeons fall dead without ever a move, but let an injured one attempt to reach security beneath some palleted stacks and she should have it without needing to be told.

She should possess a knowledgeable working relationship with ferrets, but stoats, mink and weasels (all cousins of the ferret) she should kill to order. There is much more: suffice to say her training is very contradictory not to mention confusing. It is expecting too much for complete perfection in every task. Humans can't even work that well. Remember the vermin dog is a jack of all trades. As such a slight margin of imperfection may be allowed – but only very slight. A good dog does amazing things for a man's reputation; so does a bad one, which is perhaps why so many modern pesters avoid using dogs.

Before leaving the subject of training, allow me to pass on a couple of tips. The young dog will be old enough to kill rats before she is able to run down and catch rabbits. Be patient. Avoid starting her on rats. Spend the time perfecting her retrieving of stuffed rabbit skins. After she is catching and

17

retrieving unharmed rabbits she may be entered to rats. Those who enter to rats first may end up with a dog which is hard mouthed on rabbits and reluctant to retrieve them, having been trained not to carry rats. I keep saying 'she'. Don't let this put you off male dogs. My only reason for preferring females is the fact that a 'strain' can be maintained. When she is slowing down she can be bred from, retired and a bitch pup kept to replace her and to continue the strain. Let's face it, if you are retiring an expert dog there is no sense in buying in an unproven replacement. To breed from her does not guarantee another paragon but it certainly ups the chances. Furthermore I feel bitches relate very well to male handlers, an important consideration in view of the bond needed to make a first class dog/man partnership.

6

Ferrets

The ferret is simply a long since domesticated variety of the wild polecat. Misconceptions, fallacies and fear abound in the layman's knowledge of ferrets and ferreting. This was in no way helped by a so-called expert whose hopelessly untamed ferret savagely bit an interviewer on live television. Ferrets treated like kittens will quickly become as tame and playful as kittens. Contrary to ancient belief, ferrets need not be half-wild and half-starved to work properly. Indeed, such an animal would be worse than useless. Their polecat ancestry is enough to make ferrets work; that instinct needs no sharpening by hunger. Ferrets worked hungry will simply kill a rabbit or rat underground and refuse to surface until they are no longer hungry.

Ferreting tends to be looked upon as a passing phase which country boys go through, an amateurish pastime not to be stooped to by the professional. In truth the professional ferreter, using good stock and country know-how, can achieve clearance in a time very few other methods can look at.

Main pest control uses for ferrets are in persuading rats and rabbits to forsake their burrows or other shelters to be caught in purse nets or by the dog. This must be done silently so that the occupants know only of the enemy within and nothing of the danger without.

Females (jills) are generally smaller than the males (hobs) and an ideal number for the pester to keep is three jills and one hob. Jills and hobs have different jobs and are called 'bolters' and 'liners' respectively.

Bolting

Bolters, of course, are those ferrets sent down to force the rats or rabbits to bolt out. Only the smallest bolters should be used in rat burrows. Rats are no mean exponents of self defence and it is only fair that the jill used to bolt rats should be small and wiry enough to manoeuvre easily in the narrow burrows. In practice, many jills become rat shy once bitten. They will flush out rats like the best of them but will emerge without having moved or killed any rat which has stood its ground. Every now and then the pester is blessed with a fast little jill which delights in a good scrap. Here is a gift from the gods, worth its weight in gold. However, even such a paragon should seldom be sent to ground in summer when doe rats will defend their young. Winter is the pester's main ratting season and it is then ferrets see most of their work.

Even against rabbits I prefer to use the smallest of jills for bolting. A stronger animal might easily hold back a rabbit which is trying to bolt. On the other hand I have entered a heavyweight hob to rabbits which have resisted a small jill for some minutes, resulting in full nets within seconds of his disappearance below ground.

By selectively breeding one's own stock it should be possible to produce bolters which are reluctant to stay with immovable rabbits. Liners, on the other hand, should be reluctant to leave any rabbit.

Liners

On the mention of liners we come to the job of the heavy hobs. In days gone by, before the advent of the electronic 'bleeper' or locator, the liner was kept in the carrier until the jill below was unable to move a stubborn rabbit. Whenever such a hold up occurred a cord line would be clipped to the hob's collar and he would be entered at that burrow nearest the bumps and thumps of the 'lie-up'. As often as not he would drive the jill off the rabbit and she would emerge. If the cord hadn't gone in too far it might be decided to follow it with a narrow bladed spade (graft or dibe) to withdraw the rabbit. Ferreted rabbits often run to the blind end of a burrow and bunch up their haunches to block the tunnel and prevent the ferret getting to their necks. This means the difference between a scratched rump or death for the rabbit, and is thus an effective defence. Digging to the hob can be very worthwhile as four, five or more rabbits may be found shunted nose to tail at the end of the line.

There are still many situations where a line is useful but it has largely been replaced by the electronic ferret locator or 'bleeper'. This ingenious piece of equipment consists of a tiny transmitter on the ferret's collar. This sends a continuous signal to the handset which emits a bleeping note even when the ferret has gone down several feet. By picking up the signal and slowly turning down the volume the ferreter is soon able to 'crown' the spot under which the ferret lies. A vertical shaft is dug and hey presto!

How many at Home?

Apart from being a productive way of clearing rats and rabbits, ferreting has another very useful aspect to it. Through long experience of evicting the occupants of all sorts of warrens, the ferreter eventually acquires the ability to

7 *Using electronic ferret locator.*

21

8   'Polecat ferret Hob'.

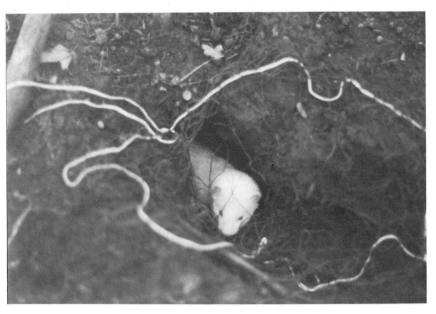

9   Rabbit purse net and bolter.

look upon a number of burrows and, by considering their appearance and the time of the year, make a fairly accurate estimate of just how many rats or rabbits will be in residence. Even the approximate adult to young ratio may be guessed. This skill can be acquired in no other way. This means that an outdoor rat survey done by a rodent controller who does not use the old methods cannot be as accurate as one done by an experienced ferreter. Buyer beware!

Rabbiting

As stated earlier there is ferreting and then there is ferreting. It can be a sport for the amateur or a skilled method of the professional. The difference is in the results. To me a professional catcher (of any wild animal) is the man who boasts not of large numbers caught but pays more attention to the number missed. By analysing the reasons for each and every escape and by using the lessons gained to prevent future misses, the amount of misses will become less and less, the catches more and more. People ferreting for sport will go to a wood and head straightway for the easiest warren to ferret – a big open one with no brambles or whins to snag the nets, no tree roots to prevent digging, no piles of cut branches to impede the dog, no waist high nettles to sting the ferreter. The man seeking control rather than sport must start at the downwind end of the wood. Yes, that old rubble pile under impregnable briars and no room to move for the surrounding elder scrub. Somehow he must ferret them out of this fortress and net, shoot or dog them all: then he will block up the holes before moving upwind to the next warren. This he will ferret out next. Any misses will run back, find their escape blocked and be caught by the dog, or run forward to the warrens yet to be ferreted. So, if all goes well the far end of the wood will eventually be reached, and the last warren ferreted and blocked. If assistance is available all warrens can be gassed before blocking (gassing should never be done by one man on his own). To gas without ferreting is to waste a harvestable rabbit crop, and is therefore less justifiable, and anyway gassing on its own is not the lethal method most farmers think it to be. Much depends upon the soil type. Some modern farmers don't seem able to see past chemical methods – witness the gallons of stuff they spray across the countryside. Sometimes I gas, sometimes I ferret, often I do both: it all depends on the job.

Free Ferrets

Alex McCurry, a part time Warwickshire vermin controller, has told me of a wild polecat he caught alive and kept in captivity. His description of the intensely wild behaviour of this animal (being incredibly fierce and shy at the same time) made me realise just what a long and thoroughly successful programme of domestication has been necessary to bring about the docile ferret we know today. Contrary to popular opinion lost ferrets do not 'turn wild'. If they are properly tamed and happy to be handled before being lost, they will be just the same after months of free range life. It is almost impossible to lose a ferret on the close confines of a rat job. Those very few ferrets which a pester might lose during his working life will therefore almost certainly acquire their freedom on rabbit jobs. Finding itself in an area full of rabbit warrens no self-respecting ferret will stray very far, even over the course of some months. In reality they can be recovered long before that.

Unlike the prolific mink, ferrets seem to find breeding difficult in the wild. Mink tend to follow burns, rivers and other watercourses so stand a good chance of meeting one another. Ferrets on the other hand will not stray at all if they have a source of rabbits and somewhere to get a drink. For that reason there need to be a lot of ferrets lost or released in one area before they can establish a feral colony. I have seen evidence of a small feral colony on Islay and have heard of them elsewhere. Even those feral ferrets had not regained the wildness of their polecat ancestors and some were unable to avoid even the trickle of traffic on the quiet island roads.

Ratting

So, having explained how well the ferret has been domesticated and yet how much natural instinct has been retained, we come to an aspect of ferreting which calls upon both their steadiness and their ferocity – ratting.

Wherever the dog's nose has silently told of inaccessible rats, it is the job of the ratting ferret to make those rats face dog, gun, nets or sticks. She (for only small females are suitable) may be asked to flush rats from stacked straw, palleted bags of grain, piles of farmyard junk or a hundred other fortresses. In this example I will describe the simple ferreting of rat burrows in soil.

You have approached the warren silently and, as always, from downwind. The ferret box is set down some distance before the holes, beyond earshot of the rats lest their eager scrambling and scratching warn the rodents. (Note - some folk call a burrow a hole, a set of holes a burrow, and a number of inter-connected burrows a warren. To avoid confusion let me clarify my use of terms: one hole is a burrow and one set of burrows is a warren. More than one warren is simply a number of warrens!) Before entering the jill, inspect the short runs joining burrow to burrow and the longer runs joining warren to warren. The runs do not matter if you intend to place purse nets over the holes. However, nets over the holes means noise over the warren, as rats must

10 *Spade, probe, locator, .410 shotgun, ferret carrier, nets line and rabbits.*

be killed immediately they are netted. Rats are very vocal and it is better to let them get clear of the holes and halfway along the runs to the neighbouring warrens before intercepting them. That way there should be no noise near the warren. Working alone, as most verminmen do, I tend to lie the dog to one side of the ferreted warren while I kneel, stick at the ready on the other side. When doing this the dog should be on the most likely side to be used by bolting rats i.e. guarding the nearer of the two neighbouring warrens. If both next door warrens are equally close to the one under attack the dog should be on the downwind side if possible. As in rabbiting it is best to start ferreting downwind and quietly seal up each ferreted warren before moving to the next.

So, dog and man are as statues on the runs. The fiery ratting jill has been slipped into the warren. She disappeared with a quiver of her brush and a quiet chatter, a sure sign of rats below. All is still.

Within half a minute a ratty face peeks from the hole nearest the dog. If anything the dog becomes even more still. She has learned the exact distance a rat must be allowed to run before it has no chance of turning back in to escape the dog. Rats' eyes can only detect movement. There is none so the rat bolts and in seconds is lying dead on the sward while the dog has become a statuette again. Now the ferret is in the heart of the warren and the bolts come thick and fast. The dog can often deal with three at a time without risk of missing any. The stick cannot hope to match these lightning canine reactions but should certainly stop far more than it misses. Having ferreted all warrens, no more than a quarter of the colony will remain alive to be treated with rodenticide. Ferreting before baiting drastically reduces the amount of poison needed and gives instant results as opposed to the days most poisons require.

Escape Drills

All rat colonies have prearranged procedures to be adopted upon a stoat, weasel (or ferret) entering the warren. As stated these normally consist of bolt holes leading along runs to the next warren. Sometimes, however, their drills can be far more elaborate. Rats on waterside banks will shoot straight down the bank to make a frogman style escape. One winter there was a particularly bad warren on the side of a flight pond. Waste potatoes and barley had been dumped there to encourage the wild duck but had been far more successful in staving off the natural winter mortality among rats. A few days after the first frosts of the year had iced over the pond I had the idea of ferreting that warren. You should have seen the pandemonium as they fled the ferret only to find themselves running on the spot on the ice. My leggy lurcher tried

26

frantically to keep her feet as she skidded around after them. If you've never seen a whippety dog trying to shake a rat while standing on smooth ice, you've never lived!

Another waterside warren was in the downwind corner of a large manmade lake. All manner of flotsam and jetsum washed into this corner to create a tightly packed log jam over which the rats would skip like Canadian lumberjacks to escape their ferreted fortress. Naturally they hadn't reckoned on any fox or other four-footed foe being able to do likewise: enter the same leggy lurcher! Not only was there a floating raft atop the water, but the wind-assisted waves had whipped up a frothy white foam into which the game little dog plunged when any timbers could support rat but not dog. She finished up bedraggled, soaking and whitewashed from head to toe, but a scattering of similarly white rats dead on the bank told of her success.

Most bizarre of all rat escape procedures was a rubble warren in the grounds of a maltings. Each and every rat flushed from that warren emerged from a bolt hole beneath an elder scrub, where there was no room for the dog to get them. Scrambling up the scrub, they gained the lower branches of an old holly tree and from there climbed to the topmost twigs where they sat motionless, hoping their attacker would neither scent nor see them. On this occasion my rifle was loaded with .22 shot which effectively turns a rifle into a miniature shotgun. All went well until I finally ran out of ammunition. Now there was nothing I could do but helplessly watch them scramble aloft. Having watched one or two, I became so frustrated I resolved to shake the tree when the next one was half way up in the hopes of dropping it to the dog. You've guessed it! The damn thing fell straight for me. Momentarily rooted to the spot, I felt it bounce off my shoulders. That we killed it owed more to panic stricken self-defence than to any professional expertise. And yet without the three part team of man, dog and ferret, that rat and his tree climbing kin would have required a lengthy poisoning or trapping programme to clear up. As it was each and every one of them lay dead beneath the holly before the little ratting ferret again showed its face.

7

Traps, Nets and Snares

I can understand some pesters not wishing to endure the 'encumberance' of dog ownership. However, I can't see why so few see fit to include basic trapping among their skills. Agreed, trapping may not fit in with the space-age image some firms like to promote. Furthermore there is the need of an old hand to learn from. Trapping is also an aspect of the job which requires the practical naturalists' ability to read animal signs. Perhaps some pesters feel embarrassed at setting a trap and visiting it day after day without result. That is all part of the learning process. Results will not come immediately.

I do not pretend trapping is an easy skill to master. It is an important part of the job, however, and he who does not master trapping does not master his job. Sometimes there is an access hole through which it is known a rat or mustelid will come after dark, or a particular rafter or run he is known to follow each night. He may be coming to a dripping tap to drink. He may have cached food in a certain corner. All of these instances are very simple and straightforward trapping jobs which should produce a cure by dawn. It is sheer neglect to attempt to use any slower method. By using all methods, old or new, the pester can choose the best one in any given situation. Look at it this way: today's multi dose rat poisons can take seven to ten days to work. Indoor rats can cause a lot of 'Disease, Damage and Distress' in that time. Traps are the answer: no waiting and no after-poison odour beneath the floor. I do not suggest the pester does not lay the usual poison in such a case. In the unlikely event of the traps failing to catch within ten days, the poison will have worked. My philosophy is not 'craft instead of chemistry'. In all cases it is 'craft as well as chemistry'. Encompass all methods.

Spring traps such as the Fenn Mk IV vermin trap need no bait, and, if properly set, kill instantly. Their main uses are against 'ground vermin' i.e. rats, stoats, weasels and mink. Cage traps will entice the quarry to enter for the bait inside. A treadle or bait hook is activated by the forager and the door slams down behind. Cage traps come in all sizes for all sizes of quarry, e.g. fox, cat, squirrel, mink.

Unless, you want a noisy half-caught rat dragging a trap around at midnight, avoid the cartoon-like giant mouse traps euphemistically called 'breakback' traps. They are not a tool for the professional. Spring traps such as the Fenn do not require baiting. They rely for their efficiency upon the pester's ability to predict where his quarry will pass. Cage traps of course do need bait. A simple way of baiting is to trace the food source your visitors are using. Rearrange things to make all this food inaccessible to them: all, that is apart from the little you use to bait the cages. For example, I recall a pigeon fancier whose valuable racers were being regularly visited by a stoat. He actually moved his beloved birds into his house for safety! A dead pigeon left over from Mr Stoat's previous attack was used to bait the trap. Next time he came a-hunting there was but one pigeon in the loft. He wasn't to know it was baiting a cage.

Similarly there are those cardboard cartons containing packets of potato crisps. Frequently shops and pubs stack the boxes up like shelves. Each box has a large hole cut in it to enable packets to be sold straight from the boxes. It is not unknown for a nocturnal rat to inspect such boxes, select his favourite flavour, then drag a packet away to his dining room beneath the floor. The obvious answer here is to call at closing time, empty all the ground level boxes, set your spring trap immediately inside the opening of a box, then empty a packet of crisps farther into the box. Rat must cross the trap to get at the crisps. Just before opening time the trapper returns and removes the trap and dead rat: a tricky job made simple.

There we have two examples, one of spring trapping, one of cage trapping. In both instances only one trap was set for one individual pest. There are, of course, jobs where numerous traps are set, usually spring traps. Here we come to true trapping i.e. the siting of a cross-country 'trap line'. Rabbit spring traps such as the Imbra, Juby and Fenn must be set just inside burrow entrances. Fenn vermin traps for small ground vermin – usually set for game protection – must be set in natural or improvised tunnels, or covered in some other way to ensure safety to non pest species. Trap lines may meander for several miles in this latter case. Nonetheless, they must be checked daily though twice daily is better for rabbit traps – just after dark and just before light. Trapping rabbits has, however, become unpopular since the demise of the pre-myxomatosis trade in rabbit meat and pelts, not to mention the banning of the non-killing gin trap. Today's rabbit traps may be humane but they are expensive, bulky, awkward to dig in and slow to produce results, due to disturbance of the burrow mouths. This brings us to snaring, which is still a favoured method of controlling rabbits and, to a certain extent, foxes.

Snares are ancient devices of the simplest design and their siting seems simplicity itself. All that's required is the ability to position a wire noose in exactly the correct place to close around the neck of the rabbit. By setting four inches above a well-worn rabbit run this should be easily achieved. It sounds simple!

Complete snares cannot be bought, unfortunately, so there is the problem

11 Snare making materials.

12 Brick removed from makeshift tunnel to reveal rat caught in fenn trap.

of having to make your own. Having cut pins and pegs and assembled and weathered your snares there come other problems. Beginners seem to have the utmost difficulty in making the snare stand steady against wind and rain. They also discover there is a knack to shaping the noose in such a way that it wants to stay open. And as snares are usually out in the open there is the difficulty of finding them all next time round; which incidentally must be at least once a day but is usually twice i.e. at first and last light. With a good teacher these points should quickly be mastered and snaring will be found to be unexpectedly humane and effective against rabbits and foxes.

Very occasionally snares are used against hares and rats. The type set for rats resembles the bent branch trap so favoured by directors of Tarzan films! The single strand brass wire noose when pulled from its anchor by a rat, is flicked upwards by a hazel or bamboo 'bender'. This snare's killing jerk is necessary as rats don't run fast enough to be killed by a normal ground snare.

The DIY skills needed to make snares will also be handy for anyone hoping to use nets. To tell the truth there are many pesters who buy their nets nowadays. Prior to the recent upsurge of fieldsports equipment suppliers, most folk made their own. It is all a question of what price you put on your time. You may feel buying is cheaper that tying. Anyone who wishes to knit their own won't learn how from this or any other book. Like so much in this job it is vital to be taught by an experienced hand. Ignoring the making of nets therefore, let us go straight onto their various uses by the verminman.

Purse nets take their name from the draw string pouch. These small nets are just large enough to drape over a rabbit hole. A hardwood peg holds both ends of the draw string. When bolted into the net by a ferret, the rabbit finds itself caught as the meshes draw closed around it. Purse nets come in smaller or larger sizes for rat and fox. Rat purses can be bought, but it is better to make your own – but make them tough. Rats bite viciously when netted and even strong nylon needs repairing after a time.

Long nets are the other commonly used pesters' net. Staked out at night to cut off feeding rabbits from their warrens they can be over 100 yards long and two feet deep. Similar to very long tennis nets with supporting sticks every seven paces, they take a lot of handling on the dark windy nights which favour their use. Unlike tennis nets they must never be tight. Lots of loose 'bagging' is needed to prevent the speeding rabbits bouncing off. Only the line along the top is taut. In the darkness very little can be seen but by holding this line anything struggling in the meshes further along can be felt.

No one goes to the trouble of setting out a long net in complete darkness unless it is known where a very concentrated number of rabbits is feeding out. Since myxomatosis arrived in the fifties, there are fewer and fewer warrens of enough size to justify nocturnal long netting. My own rabbit long net sees far more use during ferreting or rabbit driving operations by day. Seldom is it necessary to run out its entire length by day but it is simple enough to use in varying lengths. This is also true of rat long nets which need only be long enough to surround the average hen hut or garden shed. A foot tall is high enough for rat nets and it helps if the stakes have a flat base on which to stand as they must often be set in yards and on other hard surfaces. It goes without saying that rat meshes are far smaller (1 inch) than rabbit meshes (2 inch).

Net work is an important aspect in the training of a vermin dog. Even if the dog never masters the intricacies of driving rabbits to the long net or gate net by night, it must learn never to interfere with netted animals. Imagine your dog shaking a rat in a net it had taken you over an hour to knit. Though admittedly my present dog holds netted rabbits still until I can get to them.

Having mentioned gate nets, I'd better explain that they are simply nets some 3 feet high and long enough to cover most field gateways. Normally used at night against hares and rabbits, they are particularly effective where good hedges and walls force ground game to come and go via the gates. By day they are also useful for covering spaces between warrens whilst ferreting. It is far easier to train a dog for gate netting as opposed to long netting. There isn't the same problem of time wasted in getting yourself to the netted quarry (and possibly netted dog). This gives the handler greater control over the job (and hopefully the dog). Finally, there is, of course, the use of sheet netting for bird proofing. Unlike nets for catching, this rot proof 1 inch mesh netting must be stretched very tightly and fixed to the front of buildings in such a way that it will repel birds without catching them.

Wire netting also finds a use in proofing; usually it is bunched up and forced into pipe ends and similar points where rodents or birds might gain access. Wire wool is often used for the same purpose but here we are straying from netting to proofing which is already a well understood principle and needs no advice from me.

8

Guns and Ammunition

This chapter was going to be entitled 'the Verminmans' Guns', but in truth ammunition is as important, if not more so. Even during my gamekeeping days the gun I habitually carried was my .22 rifle: it still is. (The .22 rifle should not be confused with the .22 air rifle which is less of a tool of the professional.) No doubt the little .410 shotgun and its big brother the 12 bore see just as much use in rural pest control. I possess both sizes of shotgun but only use them for specific jobs. My old semi automatic .22 is my general purpose gun, the one I like to keep handy for workaday tasks. Years ago it cost £12 secondhand from one of the beaters on our shoot. That £12 is less than it costs for the firearms licence to use it. How many times over the little rifle has repaid that small outlay I couldn't imagine. The secret of its success lies in the variety of .22 ammunition available. My own choices are subsonic hollow points for general field work, .22 shot for sparrow or rats and CB caps for indoor roosting feral pigeons. These two bullets and one cartridge allow a wide range of use from sparrow to fox.

The same variety is found in shotgun cartridges. They start with lightweight loads in 2″ long cases for the .410 and go up through 2½″ and 3″ before reaching the myriad of 12 gauge rounds intended for everything from pigeon to geese, foxes and other heavyweights.

By using a .410 adaptor in one barrel of the twelve it is again possible to use one gun for all jobs – rats to foxes.

All verminmen possess at least one .22 rifle and one 12 gauge shotgun. If deer regularly figure in his work he may also keep a .243 or .270, being the common rifle sizes for roe, fallow and red deer management. With deer rifles, in common with the others, choice of ammunition is more important than model or make of gun. Indeed, as his guns come in for some tough work and rough weather, it is not unusual, for reasons of practicality and price, to buy second hand. Like all tools they must pay for themselves. Nothing fancy is required, so long as it is sound enough. As I stated my own .22 rifle has long since paid for itself, its bullets and its licences over the years. Being 'semi-automatic' means the gas recoil of each shot throws back the bolt, flicks out the empty case and pushes the next round into the breach as the bolt closes. With a five shot magazine this enables six shots to be taken in quick succession. Six are seldom necessary but self loading rifles of this type are far more useful for vermin work than the usual single shot or 'bolt action' rifles favoured by sportsmen and target enthusiasts. Numbers is the name of the game. All chances of a shot, sporting or sitter, must be taken. In all cases the first shot should kill but it is only humane to keep your aim on and be ready with the second or even a third shot if need be. This type of shooting causes very few lost 'runners'.

Mention of shooting brings us from the guns to their actual use. No one wants to know the man who is an unsafe shot. Although there may be but a second within which to take a particular shot the pester must consider the background. Could anyone be there? Could the shot damage the customer's property in any way? When hit, where will the pest fall? Will it be retrievable? He should never be tempted to shoot if he has any doubts at all.

Nor is it enough just to aim generally at the pest in question. The object of the exercise must always be a clean kill. Only half of any target – the head, neck and chest – will give that result. The whole idea of guns is to enable a kill without the need to get close to the quarry. This means most gun work is done at a fair distance, making retrieval of any injured prey a difficult task. Shooting without a dog is not a thing I like to see. In any event the speedy tracing and despatch of any shot pest is a must. It matters not if there is the chance of further shooting; the rest must be forgotten until the one that has been shot is accounted for. There is no culling method more instant or humane than a well aimed shot. However, the type of weapon and ammunition must always be the right ones for the job in hand.

13 Front to rear — CB caps, .22 subsonic and "sparrowmail", .234 round, .410 and 12 guage shotgun cartridges.

14 Modern air rifles are ideal for some pest control jobs.

15 *Parker Hale "Midland" .243 rifle for fox/deer.*

36

PART TWO

9

Rodents

Did you know that 40 per cent of all mammal species are rodents? What's more there are approximately 1650 species of rodents worldwide. How lucky we are, therefore, that only three species trouble us in Britain, namely the common or brown rat, house mouse and field mouse. (The voles will be dealt with later.) Rodent problems occur throughout the year but winter, with its hard weather, rising water tables, falling cover and failing food supply brings them into the farm buildings and cottages en masse. This annual invasion begins with the 'post-harvest influx' whenever the combines rumble into action. Subsequent stubble burning and ploughing persuades a few more to forsake the outdoor life. The final and most determined wave of this winter invasion is brought about by the first few consecutive night frosts. Isolated sub-zero nights have little effect but the magic number seems to be three. It seems three freezers in a row are enough to convince them winter has arrived to stay!

I've already mentioned Disease, Damage and Distress, our prime reasons for killing pests. Rats and house mice are unusual among pests in being guilty of all three 'D's'.

Disease

At one time leptospiral jaundice was known as rat catchers' yellow and caused a high mortality rate among Victorian ratters. Occupational hazards have reduced considerably since then but any modern pester dealing with rats must constantly bear leptospirosis in mind. Never touch damp surfaces with your bare hands where rats are active. Leptospiral virus in the rats' urine will not dry out in such conditions. It just lies there, waiting to find a scratch or cut on the hand of any passing human. The routine inoculations all pups receive at 12 weeks of age include the leptospirosis vaccine. All dogs should be injected, but it is particularly important to ensure ratting dogs get theirs. Pesters breed ratting dogs and ferrets from long lines of working parents, so there is, I believe, a certain inherited immunity in these 'working strains'.

Nevertheless, inoculations are a must for dogs and I have even had ferrets treated in the past.

Rats have been proved to carry numerous diseases but leptospirosis and distemper are the two of most relevance to the pester, his dog and ferrets.

Damage

As regards 'Damage' from rodents, here we talk of physical damage caused by gnawing water pipes (flooding) and electrical wiring (fire risk). Then there is food wastage which greatly exceeds the amount rodents actually eat. Their droppings, urine and cast hairs see to that. I remember a distraught stranger appearing on my doorstep one Sunday. He was an Edinburgh solicitor who had converted an old farm cottage into a beautifully furnished weekend home. Apparently there had been lots of evidence of rats but he had failed to recognise it. Now it was too late. The rats had gnawed into the plumbing and flooded the place in his absence. I'll always remember arriving at the cottage to find carpets draped everywhere, over the hedge, fence, garage, you name it! Furniture stood all over the lawn as the elderly couple busied themselves with mops. As you can imagine neither the couple nor their carpets ever fully recovered from the episode.

I have also seen beer raining through a pub ceiling when rats gnawed into the attic beer pipes. Being flooded with beer may appeal to some folks but it's no joke in reality. Many electricians will tell of mice found dead and stuck fast to the wiring of appliances where their last gnaw stopped not only the appliance but also the mouse. Rats beneath floors or in roof spaces will gnaw almost anything, insulated wiring included! Apart from causing numerous blackouts I wonder how many fires of 'unknown cause' were started by mice or rats? There are various amazing estimates of worldwide food loss to rodents per year. Most of the damage occurs to stored cereals. It is in this cause that most of the pester's farm yard ratting is carried out.

Distress

Last (but not least to those who suffer from it) – Distress. Fear of rodents is not confined to the female of our species. Several farm workers of my acquaintance are terrified of rats! Science fiction paperbacks and films concerning man-eating rat hordes do nothing to help these people: mind you, the hysteria engendered is good for business.

Prevention

Apart from the three D's there is the legal reason for waging war against rodents. The Prevention of Damage by Pests Act of 1949 makes occupiers and owners of all properties responsible for any form of pest infestation. Prevention is better than cure of course. Rodent proofing is often impracticable but for what it's worth there's a wealth of information available from your local pester. What is far more important is the state of affairs rodents find once inside. Farms, small holdings and the like vary enormously in their attractiveness to rodents. As I always say to farmers 'You keep it clean and I'll keep it clear'. Food (stored grain etc.) should never be situated alongside potential harbourage (stacked straw etc.). The further rodents must travel from harbourage to food source, the more options are open to the pester. Even the way in which farm animals are fed (especially hens) can often sustain rodents. Changing the feeding system to prevent rodents feeding is often enough to cure the problem. Unfortunately many farmers only worry about rodents too late, when lack of forethought has already allowed them to become established. Having introduced rats and mice in general, it's now time to look at them individually as each causes differing trouble and requires differing treatments.

The Mice

As regards the mice, people who are suddenly troubled by indoor mice at the back end of the year invariably say 'the field mice are coming in for the winter'. In truth the visitors are just as likely to be house mice. House mice would be more properly described as everywhere mice, being just as at home indoors or out. Field mice are not at all happy indoors.

Let me describe both species, how to recognise them or merely the signs of them. House mice are grey, fieldmice are a lovely russet brown with white beneath.

When house mice come into your home they are there to stay. In no time at all they have found the larder or some other food source. Packets and wrappings are no obstacle; indeed, the pieces torn off are often used for nesting material. Your house heating will enable them to breed to some extent even in dead of winter. Being curious and incautious they will be glimpsed now and again as you open a cupboard door or sit quietly with a book. Their greed and nosiness makes for easy poisoning or trapping however.

Field mice on the other hand will be heard in the walls and ceilings, but will only rarely enter rooms. Seldom are they seen therefore. Usually they will ignore the larder. It seems they are only in for the heat and are quite content to continue feeding outside. This reluctance to feed indoors makes them indifferent to baits. For this reason trapping or poisoning them is a slow process. Other than making noises in our walls, field mice will enter greenhouses and remove all seeds or peas from newly sown seed trays. They are also guilty of digging up bulbs in the garden. Infuriating though their actions may be, field mice are fairly innocent creatures in comparison to house mice. When identifying indoor mouse infestations it is as well to remember that mice in farm buildings are nearly always house mice.

One give-away sign that field mice are present is the 'decorating' of poison baits. Trays of rodenticide might lie untouched in cottage roofs all summer until the post harvest influx is signalled by mysterious noises about the house. An inspection of the roof baits will show them to be piled high with all sorts of debris—insulation material, bits of paper, lumps of plaster or cement etc. Of course, this is simply an indoor variation on the fieldmouse's outdoor habit of storing excess food beneath piles of dry leaves or whatever. People store all sorts of junk in their attics and its amazing what field mice will comandeer for creating these veritable works of art. 'Field mouse fortnight', when all this activity occurs, is a period I always look forward to each autumn. Be warned however – some of the objects piled onto the baits will appear rather large and bulky to be the work of mere mice. Rats will spring to mind. The noises in the ceiling certainly sounded like rats? Don't worry, rats are clever, resilient and resourceful, but never artistic! If they want to store bait, they move bait to cover rather than cover to bait.

The rats

So rats are to be admired for their resourcefulness. Pesters are surely the only people on earth who can admire rats. To normal people, rats are only to be reviled. Their formidable expansionism, ability to spread diseases, reputation for ferocity and immunity against poisons are but a few of the reasons we regard the brown rat with awe. For the purposes of this book I am disregarding the black rat or ship rat. He was the medieval cause of the bubonic plague – the Black Death which killed one in twenty people in England in 1348–9, and half the population of London in 1665. That was before the arrival of his brown cousin on these shores, however. Competition from the brown rat, improved human cleanliness and house building methods, all sounded the death knell for the black rat. Only a very few isolated colonies are said to remain in dock areas and sea port warehouses. Personally I've only ever come across one, a juvenile, dead in a crate of bananas in a village grocers shop! Without doubt it had come from the ship which imported the fruit.

16   Rat eating — and fouling — stored grain.

17   Coypu — escapees from fur farms now live wild in several wetland sites.

18 Run made by rats along ditchside.

Anyway, back to the brown rat, thought to have been with us since 1728, now as widespread and successful in Britain as it has become across the rest of the world. It hasn't colonised all these countries without assistance. In all cases it has been unwittingly introduced by man, the trader. This close association with us increases to reliance during bad winters. People often ask me if they should buy a cat or dog to deter rats. The truth of the matter is, rats just won't be deterred. Their persistence is the biggest problem. I even recall an instance of rat signs beneath an occupied ferret hutch! Yes, rats may even appear fearless to the point of stupidity. Fearless they may seem at times, but I've yet to come across a stupid one.

Like field mice, when rats are being encountered in dwelling houses it is most unlikely they are confined to the place. There will always be signs of rat activity outside such houses. If there isn't I would advise raising a few floor boards to see if the rats have burrowed up through the foundations from a broken or uncovered drain somewhere. Unlike mice, the brown rat is a thirsty creature to whom a ready source of water is as important as a reliable food supply.

So now you know all about rodents and the trouble they cause. But what you really want to know is 'How does the pester get rid of the blighters?' There is no easy answer. A good verminman has numerous old and new methods from which he can select the best combination of actions for any given rodent problem. I propose to outline the common situations from which the verminer may be asked to clear rodents. As will be seen, each requires a different approach.

Rats Around the Farm

Alongside rabbits and moles, farm rats are the verminmans' bread and butter. During the long hot days of summer they live out in the countryside, building up their numbers along streams, ditches, drains, fieldbanks or anywhere else where reliable food and water sources are found. Although rats don't bother too much with the farm steadings during summer, it is vital to deal quickly with any which do come on the scene. At this time of year a doe rat may litter every 10 weeks and each litter reaches breeding age at twelve weeks.

So, constant year round protection is required at farm steadings. (There are very few farmers who will pay for the time a pester would need to seek and kill the outlying rat colonies.) Rat poison is set at numerous strategic points around and within each steading e.g. in and between the sheds, barns, granaries, feed mills, driers, strawsacks, hay lofts, grain bins and other potential rat haunts. These poison points must be constructed in such a way as to be dog proof, child proof, cat proof, stock proof, weather proof and even sparrow proof. Many pesters site their baits in lengths of 5'in' diameter pipes along the foot of walls and other edges which rats will follow. I do this myself but it has to be borne in mind that most farms are only visited monthly or six weekly so the bait points must contain enough rodenticide to last until the next visit. In many positions pipes are not the answer and a larger bait point must be improvised beneath an old door, corrugated metal sheet, wooden pallet etc. The staff, of course, must be made aware of this and warned not to uncover the bait.

Once you have a minefield of bait points established, any resident rats should quickly perish. Of course, the base ingredient of your baits must compete favourably with the various cereals and animal foods around the place. Where rats are not feeding well enough on the multi-dose bait points it may be necessary to use a single dose bait. Brodifacoum is perhaps the safest single dose poison available at present, in that the one fatal dose does not affect the rat until several days have elapsed. So, if it is found that a dog has managed to get at some bait there is time for the vet to give the vitamin K1 antidote. If the farm is just an absolute mess with food scattered everywhere, poisoning can be difficult. In addition to the permanent bait points it may then be necessary to set a few Fenn Mk 4 spring traps. Like the poisons, traps must be safely covered, but this must be done in such a way that the rats' suspicions will not be raised. The law requires these traps to be checked daily but most farmers will think twice about paying for daily visits. Usually there is an interested and keen farm hand among the staff who is only too happy to look after the traps. Several such people assist me around the farms and some have become excellent trappers. In addition to the rodenticide baits it may be beneficial to site one or two poultry drinkers containing a soluble rodenticide in water. In dusty locations such as farm granaries these will be readily used by the rats and I have seen some very impressive results gained with them, especially in summer.

All this continuous precautionary baiting and trapping will mean very few rats around the steading. Here the vermin dog comes into its own. People tend to imagine the pesters' dog is only called upon when seething hordes of rats are encountered. Nothing could be further from the truth. Routine ratting can be much less dramatic. The pester arrives for his regular service of the steading. Torch in one hand, bucket of rodenticide in the other and dog loosely at heel he will go round the bait points, topping them up where necessary. Any dark corner, stack of sacks, hutt of bales or other places a rat may be hiding will quietly be checked by the dog's nose. Any likely place she misses only needs to be pointed out with the quiet request 'In there'. Seldom will any more than half a dozen rats be in a baited steading. Frequently there may be just the one. One or six, the dog will locate their whereabouts and 'mark', i.e. stand motionless, staring towards the source of the live scent. If the harbourage is small (less than twenty straw bales or fifteen sacks of grain) it may be worth moving them to allow the dog to kill the rat. As each bale, sack, drum, log or whatever is lifted it is used to construct a wall around the scene so that, as the last pieces are moved, escape for the rats has been cut off. Of course, a certain amount of plugging holes with straw etc. may need to be done. There is no hurry to flush the rats. A spectacular flush of rats is no use whatsoever if they all promptly disappear in all directions. Once all points of escape are sealed, the pester stands at one side of the remaining cover, the dog at the other. The man then slowly raises the side farthest from him, prompting the rats to run towards the dog. In a flurry of action the job is over. Two or three rats may lie dead. None should have escaped if the preparations were properly arranged.

Naturally the dog may mark rats in larger stacks or even inside walls or inaccessible cavities where they will need to be left. A well placed spring trap or a new bait point if there isn't one close by will do the trick just as well.

The Rat in the Cottage

There is no more urgent job to the verminman than rats in an occupied house. Rats gaining access to a bedroom at night will bite the lips, ears, nose or hand of anyone sleeping there. Three times I have known this happen, each time the victims were very elderly ladies. On the first occasion, which involved two old spinsters, there was a general panic and much nocturnal hullabaloo involving the night-shift police, local councillor and various odds and bods. At that point only one of the old ladies had been bitten. The assembled mass restored order, dispensed tea, and eventually left. At four in the morning the second sister was woken with a bite to the face, that in a different bedroom some hours after the first attack and regardless of the furore which had gone on between times! Need I say any more: rats in houses must always be treated as emergencies. Unfortunately today's multi-dose poisons are safe to the point of taking several days to work. As for single dose or acute poisons – rats do not tear into newly found foods: rather, they tend to nibble at it until they are sure. As this may take a day or two there is not much point setting a single dose poison such as zinc phosphide as the rats will probably take enough to cause them pain, but not death. The whole reason for the existence of multi-dose poisons is this bait shyness caused by the lethal single dose poisons. However, failings aside, the first thing the verminer should do is set multi-dose poisons (or a very slow acting single dose such as Brodifacoum) at all points including the rooms, garden, roof space and under the floor.

Hopefully the pester will be able to trap the rats long before the poisons have the chance to work. Poisoned rats in wall cavities or other hidden parts may never be detected. Dead rats can, however, be just as bad news as living ones, especially in hot summer weather. Depending upon the heat, ventilation and dampness of where the body lies, there may or may not be an odour problem. If there is, the occupant may feel the live rats were less trouble, especially if walls or floorboards need to be broken to cure the problem.

One way or another the house rat is a case in point where trapping cannot be replaced by science, Fenn Mk IV Spring traps or multi-catch cage traps are the answer every time. I prefer spring traps myself as, if cleverly sited, they don't require baiting. Obviously the large quantities of cereal-based poisons set throughout the property will detract effectiveness from a baited trap.

Beware of 'New Object Reaction': if the rats have been on the scene long enough to know where everything is. Traps suddenly appearing from nowhere will be avoided by rats to start with. Instead of 'New Object Reaction' I prefer to speak of 'New Scent Reaction' which is much nearer the mark. If the pester has kept his traps next to the carrier full of ferrets in his van, or near the dog or some odorous chemical, the rats will take an age to accept them – possibly never. If on the other hand he keeps them in a bucket of soil or even an empty box well away from strange smells, all should be well. Remember, of course, when talking of scents we mean scents detectable by rats, though possibly not by humans. Scent of dog, soap or cigarettes on your hands is enough to defeat all your best laid plans. If the rat is thought to have come on the scene only recently, there should be no new object reaction to the site of a trap so long as it is scent free.

Often when using traps in these circumstances I set them in purpose-made wooden boxes which have an entry hole for rats at each end. Be sure the boxes are scent free also. These boxes protect children and pets from the traps (and vice versa). A string handle on the lid allows customers to move the box and trap safely if the rat is seen to have moved elsewhere. Bait may be placed in the box, though the actual placing of the box is far more important than use of bait. The beauty of trap boxes is the way rats are guided onto the treadle so that a forepart catch and instant kill is guaranteed everytime. This is most important when sited in someone's house.

Garden Rats

Another very common rat job the pester is called upon to handle is that of rats in the town or country garden. Rats like gardens, because gardens are near houses, and houses mean humans. Humans like feeding the birds, keeping

46

pets in outdoor hutches, aviaries, lofts, kennels etc. tipping all manner of household waste onto what is euphemistically referred to as the compost heap, filling refuse bags and bins until they overflow. You name it, one way and another there is no shortage of food in the garden, and if there is any shortage there's always next door's place!

Other than food there are numerous fortresses in which to lodge. Favourites among these are, of course, beneath the garden shed or the car lock up. However, log piles, coal boxes, floored greenhouses and the like will suffice. And, of course, there's often all manner of junk in the form of rubble, timber and other materials which humans habitually hate to dispose of in case they one day collect enough of it to build an extension to the house!

Householders may happen to spot a rat as they swing the car into the drive late atnight. More usually no rats are seen at all. The pester may be called because one or two strange burrows have suddenly appeared. During periods of lying snow rats may be betrayed by their 'starry' footprints. Holes may be chewed in the bottom of plastic rubbish bags or bins. 'Larders' of stored food scraps in nests of torn up paper may be discovered. These and several other clues should lead any right-thinking person to phone for the nearest vermin catcher. Of all the situations in which rats occur, gardens are second only to open warrens in the countryside when it comes to opportunities to actually catch and kill the rats on the spot. Personally I feel a bit of an idiot setting a poison bait and telling a panic stricken housewife that they should all be dead within a week or ten days: and yet that is what many pest controllers do as a matter of course. The first thing the pester must do is to locate the rats. In easy cases the householder will tell how the rats have caught onto the daily bird feeding routine. When it comes to a free feed rats seem to be able to tell the time. At the appointed hour the crusts and scraps no sooner hit the lawn, the window no sooner slams shut, and Mr Rat scurries out in broad daylight to ferry all the pieces back and forth until he has them all stored beneath his harbourage. The pester hearing this story will know the rats are most probably beneath that shed or whatever, even as he stands there beside it. So if rats are reported to always come and go from a certain place, or if there is only one shelter in the garden they could possibly use; then you can say for certain where they are. If there are several potential harbours, each showing some rodent signs, it will be necessary to fetch the dog from the van. She knows all about sheds, garages, coalboxes and junk piles too! Without any bidding she will go quietly from one to the other, testing the air and ground around them with her nose, a highly sensitive piece of apparatus, the workings of which no man can comprehend.

Suddenly she stands staring at the low space under the shed. She not only knows they are under there, she also knows which corner they are nearest. 'Reading' a dog is a skill pesters have used for years before the fashionable phrase 'body language' was ever thought of. When experience has forged the teamwork between man and dog it is possible to 'read' whether hedgehog, mice, rat, cat or rabbit lies hidden there simply by watching the dog's attitude and reactions. As a simple example my present dog wags her tail slightly when marking mice but never when marking rats: mice are good fun but rats can bite back! Anyway, back to the shed. She has told you they are under there. Now open the door and let her check they have not gnawed up through the floor to take up residence inside (the interior of garden huts is often no more orderly than the garden itself). She enters, sniffs around, comes out and again takes up her statuesque mark at the far corner. Have a look all round the outside of the shed. If you were a rat forced to bolt which escape route would you choose? Along inside the hedge? Away through that long grass? Under the wheelbarrow, through the stack of plant pots and dive under next door's shed?

As explained during farm ratting, there is no problem in getting rats to vacate their lodgings. The problem lies in making sure they can be caught when they do make a run for it. If there is just too much cover and clutter near the shed, forget it. Spoon some poison under there as would your 'modern' competitor. Perhaps what cover there is can be moved without too much trouble? The idea is to isolate the shed so that all bolting rats must cross vulnerable open spaces and, even if they reach the nearest shelter, should find their entrance blocked. Rats are creatures of habit. They bolt along pre-planned escape routes. If that route is blocked midway, they find themselves at a loss and are easily caught. All preparations completed, it is decided to go ahead and clear them. Back to the van for the ferret carrier. Out with your best ratting jill, a fast, wiry and fearless litle warrior who knows her job well and is well aware of her importance as the third member of the three part man/dog/ferret team. If the space beneath the shed runs all the way round, it will be necessary to station the dog at one corner and stand yourself and your stick diagonally opposite. This way all four sides can be watched. Of course, the pester can't see the dog, but this diagonal method of ferreting small buildings is one they are both well accustomed to and, like boxers, each knows to return to his own corner after each flurry of action. By the way, it is sometimes prudent to lay a plank or two down if they are handy, thus completely sealing one or more sides of the shed if it is desired to make the rats flush in a particular direction. Of course, when using the diagonal method, the dog is always placed at the corner where most action can be expected. Right, we're in place; slip the ferret under and stand back. Make no sound or movement. Listen and watch. Within seconds, a short movement and distinctive dull rattle is heard from the other side: first kill to the dog. She gets another, you get one with your stick, and a squeal somewhere below tells the jill has killed the last one. Soon she is out, back in her box, the dead rats put in the refuse bin, the garden clutter restored to some semblance of order and most important, some rodenticide is spooned under the shed or some other likely point. This measure ensures any new rats coming on the scene will be cleared and it also serves to protect your methods from the criticism of the competitor who accuses you of 'still using ancient methods'. This way you do what he would have done, plus a lot more besides. It seems sensible to me that, if the ratcatcher is there and the rats are there, the ratcatcher should be able to catch the rats if it is at all possible. Putting down poison and walking away from them can hardly be described as progress, can it? As the reader will tire of hearing me say, 'Always use all methods'.

10

Rabbits and Hares

I will deal with rabbits first as, along with moles and rats, they constitute the country catcher's main workload. Rabbits have been such a plague upon the countryside for such a long time it is no wonder so many methods have evolved for their control. Favourites among them are snaring, lamping, ferreting, gassing, shooting, longnetting, trapping and dogging. In practice, it is normal to combine two or three methods under the one job – rabbiting. Firstly though, let me explain the basic methods before telling how they can be used in unison for best results.

Snare Making

To understand snaring it is necessary to understand the rabbits' habit of lying up in their warrens by day and venturing forth to feed by night (this habit is also exploited in lamping and longnetting). Leading from the wood, or wherever the warrens are, there will be found many little paths in the grass or indeed on any soft surface. Closer examination of these runs will reveal each to consist of a dotted line of worn pads along which the rabbits hop as if using stepping stones. Along these runs the rabbits come under cover of darkness, and on these runs, if properly set, the pester's snares will catch them. The typical rabbit snare, of which it is unusual to set any less than a hundred at a time, consists of six strands of brass wire twisted together to form a thin cable. With this cable a pear-shaped noose is formed approx. four inches deep by five across. An eyelet allows the noose to slide freely. This noose is anchored by a cord at least one foot in length to a hardwood peg approx. eight inches long. The exact type of hardwood used is a matter of local preference but the favourite must be ash for sheer ease of cutting and shaping. Others used are elm, elder and indeed any other hardwood which will cut from the log into straight, knotless pegs requiring the minimum of paring and shaping and possessing the quality of retaining strength despite the long wet/dry/wet existence of the snare peg.

Last but not least the start pin, star pin, pricker or tealer, whose job it is to stand unobtrusively beside the run and hold the noose in position above one of the 'stepping stones'. Starpins are normally cut from hazel. Hazel is preferred for its straightness but in truth almost any slender stick approx. ⅜-inch diameter and eight inches long will do. Soft centred sticks won't do, as they cannot be pointed. Wood which becomes dry and brittle will not do either. Willow, sycamore and ash, all in the bark, are good alternatives if there is not enough hazel to hand. At the top of the starpin a small roof shape is made with two cuts of the pester's pocket knife. The blade is then laid across this roof and gently pressed down for ¾ inch to form a tight slit the tension of which alone must be strong enough to hold the snare against any amount of wind and rain.

Snaring

Snaring is not an art, it is two arts. Having made the snares we move on to the second art – catching rabbits in them. Let us imagine a large number of runs have been found leaving a rabbit-riddled wood, and leading out into the centre of an adjoining pasture. Firstly the pester checks with the farmer to ensure no stock is due to be turned onto the grass for at least four days. Next he goes into the field, about fifteen yards or so, depending on the strength of the runs. Now he walks parallel to the fence and sets a snare on each run as he crosses it. More than one snare may be set on a run but, if so, they shouldn't be any closer than fifteen feet. On very short turf the runs may be all but invisible. In such cases the snarer should work into the sun, preferably early or late when it is low in the sky. Then even the faintest of runs will become apparent. Once when setting snares I saw a rabbit run over a brow. The poor soil, heavy grazing by sheep and rabbits, and a prolonged drought had turned the turf into a pale yellow stubble no deeper than the fur on a bumble bee. There was no discernable run whatsoever, but I had not taken my eye off the route the rabbit had taken. The snare looked ridiculous and very conspicuous on that barren sand paper. Next day it looked a hundred times better, having cleanly and quickly killed what I believed to be the same rabbit. Although rabbits at times appear to travel without using runs, rest assured it is only you who can't spot the runs; the rabbits know perfectly well where they are.

Lamping

Lamping is generally the name given to a nocturnal means of taking rabbits by spotlight and lurcher dog. All that is required is a spotlight, a motorcycle battery in your pocket and a very clever dog by your side.

Rabbits which do not run from car headlights fall easy prey to motor cars. For this reason many modern people, more used to cars than rabbits, believe the latter to be mesmerised and spellbound by bright lights. Nothing could be farther from the truth! If you have never done so, take yourself out into a field by night. Stand there and count the lights across the landscape. Red and white car lights moving on distant roads. Cottage lights, farmhouse lights, village lights, everywhere lights. Wild animals are well used to seeing lights at night. In fact they totally ignore them and certainly don't associate them with danger, which is why so many are killed on our roads. Let's return to that same pasture we snared. It is now a year later and the rabbits are back in number. The feeding pasture is to the west of the woodland warrens. We await a suitable night, black as tar and with a good westerly wind: a wind which will be blowing from the feeding rabbits towards the empty warrens. Quietly the lamper gets himself and his dog to the woodside. He is now between the rabbits and their homes. They cannot see him as he moves slowly and quietly in the gloom. They cannot scent him as the wind is not in their favour. They do not know he is there. On the other hand he knows exactly where they are. The wind in the dog's face brings the tantalising scent of rabbit. She is straining eyes, ears and nose ready for the action. Switch on the light and cast the beam over the scene: a horde of grazing rabbits, their eyes reflecting ruby red. Decide upon the nearest, switch off the light ... Use your previous knowledge of this field, its rabbits and runs, to guess which part of the wood behind you this rabbit will run for. Move over to that point in the woodside hedge or fence. On with the light, settle the beam on the rabbit, hiss the dog away and keep the light over her shoulder as she creeps out. Approaching out of the beam she is invisible to the rabbit and may take it before it runs. If rabbit bolts, dog will pursue. At this point the rabbit is running into the beam. Keep the light low so as not to dazzle the dog. Pushed hard, the rabbit will twist and turn to evade capture. By now it is well off it's well known run, dazzled by the light and approaching the hedge at an unknown point. If not already caught it will be picked up by the lurcher as it tries to negotiate the hedge, bank or fence. As the dog strikes it is a good idea to shake the beam to further confuse the rabbit. Do not be fooled, dear reader, into thinking no rabbit ever escapes. Escapes are commonplace and missed rabbits become lamp shy, leaving the field en masse at the first cast of the beam on future nights. The actual chases are just as fast, hectic and spectacular in the beam as they are by day. There is certainly no mesmerising effect: I wish there was!

No, the only reason for dogging rabbits by night rather than by day is the fact that rabbits are far from home during the hours of darkness. Quite simply the farther they are from home the more chance a running dog has of catching them.

19 Snare on rabbit run showing distinct "pads" on grass.

20 Ferreting gear.

21 *Dressing snared rabbits.*

Long netting

Myxomatosis and lamping have largely been responsible for the demise of longnetting. Myxomatosis has meant that there are no longer the large numbers of rabbits present to justify the trouble of longnetting. Since myxomatosis arrived in 1953, rabbits have taken until now to stage a partial comeback. Even now the disease can decimate local populations. Nowadays rabbits can shake the disease off but the virus seems to come along in varying degrees of virulence and every now and then a killing strain hits them.

Lamping, the other reason for the reduction in longnetting, requires exactly the same situation and weather conditions necessary for long netting. Therefore, when the right night presents itself the pester can choose between lamping or longnetting that particular woodside. Long nets are very long nets – fifty, seventy or over one hundred yards long by two feet high. The setting of such a net and its numerous supporting poles in total darkness on uneven ground on a windy night is something of a daunting prospect; especially when the far simpler alternative of lamping is available. For these reasons I must confess that my long net sees far more service by day during ferreting or rabbit driving jobs. By night I only use it where continued lamping has left a large number of lamp shy rabbits. That many rabbits is very unusual despite so called resistance to 'myxy'.

Longnetting by night is a matter of silently running out the net between the rabbits and their warrens. There are then various means by which the rabbits can be made to run for home. The man on the net simply goes back and forth along the net, killing the rabbits and leaving them there to be untangled when the action is over. By day the long net may be set around large overgrown warrens to save the trouble of purse netting the individual burrows.

Shotguns

Where rabbit earths are dotted throughout open woodland, rabbit drives by a number of men with shotguns can be effective, especially immediately prior to ferreting, gassing or both. Though such drives are all the more effective when assisted by a mixed bunch of spaniels, terriers or lurchers, I must confess to some reservations about dogs on rabbit drives. Certainly I would never subject my dog to the risk, no matter how slight, of being shot.

Shotguns are also used to take rabbits bolted by ferrets in cover where netting is difficult. Bear in mind that professional ferreting should be a silent operation. Shooters should stand well away from the warren being ferreted and for safety's sake should only shoot rabbits which have gone past them.

Rifles

The .22 rifle with sound moderator and telescopic sights attached is an excellent tool for control of small rabbit populations. I emphasise the word control, not clearance. Particularly during hot summer weather when young and old rabbits graze out on their doorsteps by day, the rifle in steady hands, using the correct ammunition can take a harvesteable surplus over a period of time, enough to make up for their breeding rate.

Used in conjunction with the lamp and lurcher at night the rifle or a silenced .410 shotgun can be used to shoot any rabbits which allow a close enough approach. If they are missed or if they run before the shot, the dog can be sent to try for them.

Trapping

The rabbit traps available today are the Juby and the Fenn. The Imbra is legal but out of production. The gin trap is illegal and out of use. All legal rabbit traps kill instantly and as such are selective and humane. Rabbit trapping was once an industry of great financial importance in most rural areas. A massive market for their meat and skins in our major cities ensured continued prosperity for hundreds of rabbit catchers. Myxomatosis and the banning of the gin trap (and any spring trap set in the open or designed to hold rather than kill cleanly) brought an end to the rabbit industry. Those few part timers who continued found the new traps to be very bulky, hard to set and the imposition of having to site them inside the burrow mouths a bit too much to bear. For these reasons, rabbit trapping has unfortunately become unpopular with professionals. Another reason for the lack of enthusiasm for the new traps is their price, bearing in mind that setting less than fifty is hardly worthwhile. A price of four or five pounds per trap is a nonsense when compared to the few pence rabbit snares cost. For myself, I like to keep a few rabbit traps for odd jobs where only traps will do, but I do not number trapping among my main rabbiting methods. 'Warrener' of *Shooting News* has done wonders in renewing interest in rabbit trapping. He is a trapper with a natural empathy for the job and though he has a deep interest in all vermin control, he has a real love for the art and challenge of rabbit trapping. Perhaps through his writings the art will return to favour among verminmen. If so, the first requirement would be the return of the Imbra or some other lightweight trap to the market. Despite the foregoing difficulties the message of this book remains that the master of all methods is the man most likely to find an answer where others fail. For this reason, if for no other, I would urge all verminmen to help keep the art of rabbit trapping alive.

Combining Methods

Ferreting rabbits has been well enough covered in Chapter 6. Gassing has been discussed under Chapter 4, 11 and 16. Dogging, apart from lamping, can only be used in conjunction with the other methods. True, the verminman's dog picks up the odd rabbit most days on jobs other than rabbit jobs. This dogging of rabbits is very handy for providing ferret food and must account for a great many rabbits over the years, but it is incidental to proper rabbit work.

The most useful dogging is always carried out prior to ferreting, gassing, and trapping of the warrens. By sending the dog to hunt out those rabbits from the brambles, tussocks and cut branches, it is possible to catch one or two outliers. More important, the majority will be sent to ground, making the warren work doubly effective. Once the warrens have been cleared and blocked up, it is worthwhile dogging the area again. Any rabbits chased this time will find their front door locked and will make easy catches for the dog.

Ferreted and trapped warrens can be gassed before blocking. By day, ferreting and long netting or gate netting can be combined. By night, lamping and shooting combine well as do lamping and long netting. By carrying the rifle around the snare line a few more rabbits will be added to the bag.

As always – the more methods, the more results.

Hares

The brown hare is only a pest when numbers increase to the point of unacceptable grazing of crops. Four hares are said to eat as much as one sheep. When talking of young cereal and vegetable crops, that can amount to a lot of damage.

In many areas over recent years, the brown hare has declined under conditions of intensive factory farming, crop spraying, faster and faster farm machinery, larger and larger fields and a host of other changes to those fertile parts of their habitat.

Remembering that numbers and whereabouts (not species) is what makes a pest, there are now many localities in the UK where hares can no longer be considered a pest. Personally, I have hardly killed a hare for several years now. Those I have killed have in the main been attacking young fir plantations. Even a few hares in such plantings can deform dozens of nursery trees by nipping off the new shoots and tip or 'leader'. This results in the trees bushing outwards instead of reaching upwards.

Traditional February hare drives are something of a rarity now. Where

22 *Even small lurchers can catch hares!*

they are still held results are often far lower than in years gone by. These drives consist of a broad line of local villagers or farm lads, the only qualification being the possession of a shotgun.

It was not at all unusual for over a hundred hares to be killed on one estate in one day. Given that almost all estates and farms held weekly hare drives throughout February it all adds up to an immense national annual cull. And yet there were just as many hares there the next year. Just how insidious modern farming methods are towards wildlife is illustrated by the fact that farming, particularly spraying, has brought about the scarcity of hares which years of hare drives failed to achieve. Perhaps I should concede a victory for technology over tradition? I'm sure the hares would prefer tradition.

Control

However, in places where farming is less hyperactive, there are still good numbers of brown hares and though the numbers may not always justify hare drives, there are some control measures available to counter hare damage. Even if no damage is being done, it is better to carry out a cull outside their breeding season than to risk having to cull later when leverets are being reared.

Shotgun drives may still be necessary for the worst hare jobs, but mostly it is enough for one man with a rifle to stalk the hares early or late in the day. Gate netting can be very useful where the fields have good walls or heavy hedging. Here tennis style nets are erected over the gateways and the dog sent to hunt the hares from the field. Gate netting has always been a favourite method of the poacher and, as such, was always done by night. There is in fact no reason why gate netting should not be done by daylight although the net man must always keep well out of sight behind the walls.

Coursing

Lurchers have an inborn talent for hare catching, either by stealth or sheer speed and stamina. Although hare coursing seems to be the one fieldsport most offensive to our millions of unnatural suburbanites, I fear their opposition has little to do with concern for hares. Catch up some summer hares on any estate where winter hare drives are still carried on. Odds are you will find several carry shot in their tough backsides or even show signs of healed leg fractures, and yet most suburbanites have never even heard of hare drives. Coursing on the other hand only produces dead hares or missed hares.

Hares caught in this manner are no different from hares taken by foxes, mink, polecats, farm cats or sheepdogs. Hares will always fall to predators even after the law states that greyhounds must not number among these predators. I find lurcher coursing to be an entirely natural method of hare control. In a nation where irate viewers phone up the BBC to complain when wild lions are shown killing their dinner ('why didn't that bad cameraman do something to stop it?'), it is hardly surprising that people complain about coursing. The type of coursing shown on television always involves two dogs at a time, which is what most folk object to. These are greyhounds used for sport and bear no comparison to lurchers used for pest control which need only ever course on their own.

It is strange that the more people become divorced from nature the more they talk about 'conservation' and yet when confronted by real nature they are disgusted! What people need to realise about conservation is this: nature is all about animals living off other animals. Just as the fox lives by his ability to hunt so does the verminman. It has always been that way and no harm has come of it. Harm only comes when the threat is to the whole species, not just a few individuals. Threats of that scale can only come from habitat destruction (in this case crop spraying). Ironically, spraying, pollution and other dangers to habitat all occur in an effort to support the masses of town dwellers who are so sentimental about animals. There is no point at all in saving individual animals if you leave them nowhere to live, is there?

Before responding to any damage perpetrated by hares a glance at the calendar is important. Hares are one of the few examples of animals which can simultaneously be classed as both pest and game. This means there is a hare closed season. This restriction only applies to shooting and then only on moors, heaths and other open non-arable ground. There is also a ban on selling hares during the period March to July. As hare shooting dates vary between England, Scotland and Ireland I do not intend to list them here. They are easily obtainable by all shotgun owners from their local police.

Hares can be snared but this is rarely used as a pest control method. They do not have runs as do rabbits. Snares must, therefore, be set at gaps where hares are known to go through hedges or fences. Fence snares, though effective are not entirely selective. Anyway, snaring would only ever be considered when a small number of persistant foragers, perhaps half a dozen, were to be dealt with. An example would be hares in a large garden where their tastes in shrubs, flowers and vegetables can be interestingly consistant. Such a known small group would be more easily dealt with by stalking into range with a .22 rifle. This brings us to the common alternative to shotgun drives i.e. the use of a .22 by day or with the aid of a spotlight by night. This can either be done on foot or from an off road vehicle. (It is, of course, illegal to shoot from a public road, either from a vehicle or on foot.) I'm sure the popularity of shooting from land rovers or tractors in fields at night has more to do with the avoidance of having to carry the kill than with increased efficiency. Adult brown hares weigh between 7 and 11 pounds and it doesn't take very many to fill a game bag. However, the man who goes on foot need only cache his hares here and there near the farm roads to be picked up later. At night, going on foot, into the wind of course, allows closer shots and less disturbance to other hares in the vicinity. By day, of course, the pedestrain stalker must keep a very low profile and employ the maximum of fieldcraft. Bearing in mind the comparative lack of fear all wild animals afford to passing vehicles it will be realised that the use of a vehicle, as a sort of mobile hide, will pay dividends during the hours of daylight.

11

The Fox

Like all animals the fox can be friend or foe. On rabbit jobs I do not raise the gun if he shows his face. Where, game, lambs, or poultry are at risk his numbers must be kept down in general, particularly any troublesome individuals such as rogue lamb killers. Of course, nothing but control measures can protect unpenned game and lambs. However, hens, geese, ducks, pigeons and the like are frequently massacred at night while in their coops and lofts. Foxes seem to have a sixth sense when it comes to breaking into such places, but there is no sense in making it easy for them. People have a moral duty to make coops as fox proof as possible. Even then some foxes will get in with the inevitable result but, having taken proofing precautions the owner can then set about catching the fox without misgivings. Chemical repellents and electric fencing around pens are a good temporary measure, but will not work forever. There are ways and means of catching foxes but of all the normal pest species foxes are the most difficult to account for. It is easy to detail here the various methods. What I cannot adequately describe is the years of field experience necessary to produce a naturalist/hunter, a man who is at one with nature, for such a man is the one who will consistently catch foxes in the wild. The fox in Britain no longer has any natural enemies or even animals which compete for breeding sites. His numbers seem to be higher now than they ever have been. Blanket conifer plantations over vast tracts of land are one reason for the increase. No longer does he retreat in the face of urban spread, indeed urban and suburban breeding foxes are now commonplace in most cities. It seems that once one pair have brought up a litter in town, all the surviving cubs of the litter are 'townies' born and bred and will subsequently breed in town and produce ever-increasing numbers of urban foxes. Scavenging on man's litter largely replaces hunting, There is precious little harm town foxes can do, so I rarely advocate control. Of course, all cases differ and foxes under a building can often cause flea infestation or odour problems. On the continent the fox is the major carrier of rabies and if that fearsome disease ever crosses the Channel, our attitude to urban fox control may require reviewing. That would see a great increase in cage trapping, which is rarely used today. Normal methods of shooting and snaring cannot normally be used safely in towns due to an abundance of people, dogs and cats. However, this book only concerns country pest control so let me describe some typical fox complaints and remedies.

Mass Poultry Killing

By far the most damaging work of foxes is done when one manages to enter a hen house at night. Darkness makes the hens very vulnerable and in a small coop of up to two dozen birds almost all will be killed in one attack. Predation on this scale is only ever perpetrated by fox, mink or very rarely, a rogue badger. As in all pest control the prerequisite is to identify the culprit. The more of a practical naturalist the pester is, the easier he will find this aspect.

Having ascertained that Mr Fox is to blame, a course of action must be decided upon. Where all the birds lie dead it is unlikely the culprit will be in any hurry to return. For all he knows the slain are still there and he may be back in a week or two to collect one. Where he has only been able to reach some of them he knows where there are dead hens, fresh live hens; and, more important, he knows how to get in beside them. He will almost certainly be back.

Sometimes the pester is called in at a later stage where the fox is already making nightly visits and killing one or two hens (only because high perches or some other feature prevents him killing all at once). Persistent foxes of this type are the least difficult to deal with. It is necessary to find a vantage point overlooking the route by which the fox is expected to come. This ambush point must be downwind of the hen house and the fox's approach. Preferably it will be in a raised position possibly a window of the farm house, a knoll or a ladder against a tree. This way, even if the fox arrives from behind the rifleman any giveaway scent should go over his head. It may be neccesary to leave some of the farmhouse curtains open to allow enough light onto the scene. Be careful to ensure no one uses the rooms or is seen by the fox. Don't have a previously dark henhouse and yard suddenly flooded with light; no fox is that daft. If the line of fox approach is absolutely certain, e.g. if he is using a hole in a wire netting pen which encloses the coop, it may be possible to sit in the coop with the rifle levelled through an open window onto his point of entry into the run. However, all this advice on ambushing makes the use of a dog very difficult. Unless the success of the shot – there only is one shot – is beyond doubt, it is best to have the dog ready. That means elevated or indoor positions are out. The verminman must compromise and hide himself and dog on ground level within easy range of the path. Range here usually depends upon visibility. If there is enough light and cover, the range may be short enough to use a shotgun. Although a shotgun and heavy shot is correct for a moving fox, I personally prefer to stay as far back as the light allows. It is easy enough to have the rifle on him then emit a low squeak or whistle, at which he will momentarily stop and stare. He may then be shot and the dog released if necessary. It goes without saying that the dog must not whine or struggle to be released before the shot is fired. This the dog learns when fox 'calling', which will be described later. If the fox does not appear at the ambush there is every chance he was there, and he knew the pester was there too. No one would ever contemplate lying in ambush for a fox, except at a hen roost under nightly attack or at an occupied fox earth. Where hens are being killed with less regularity, shooting is out of the question. It is then prudent to trap or snare.

Trapping

Cage traps are the only legal method of trapping foxes (not to be confused with snaring). By that I mean there are no legal traps which will kill a fox. Nor is it legal to set leg-holding gin traps for fox or anything else. As gins were extremely common before being banned, there are still a great many of them hanging around in old farm sheds. Their use should never be considered, no matter what carnage and mass murder is found in the coup. Cage traps are often used where it is intended to transfer rather than kill an animal. Poultry killing foxes must, of course, be killed. However, if it is intended to use a trap for fox, that trap must be a cage trap. Let us imagine all the hens are dead and no new ones are being put in until the fox is caught. Remove all but one of the bodies and use that one to bait the cage. Most pesters will make their own fox cage trap as the retail versions are far too expensive for the few occasions when such a trap is ever used. Leave the cage set inside the empty hen house for as long as it takes to catch the fox. This may be some weeks, but if the original break in point has not been repaired, the fox should return eventually. Until he does, daily morning checks must be made.

Snaring

Let us assume there are still hens, ducks, turkeys or whatever alive in the attacked coup and the break-in point has been repaired to keep him out when next he visits. It is now necessary to look around outside and discover the various routes by which a fox is likely to approach. Here fox snares may be set to await him. Unlike rabbit snaring, there is no such thing as a discernable 'fox run' except within yards of the earth or den. Foxes will however use any

23 Keeping a litter fed is tiring work!

24 Fox cage traps should be baited beneath the floor.

path, track, run or other way which makes progress easier and quieter in the dark of night. The correct setting up of the snare is of vital importance to avoid the accidental catching of other animals which might use the run. The noose itself is shaped as a horizontal pear, 6 inches deep and 8 inches across. Naturally it is best set where the path narrows to 8 inches between bushes or growth. The height of this noose from the ground is varied depending upon the way he is expected to be carrying his head. On runs through heavy cover 4 inches is about right. On the few occasions when a run in the open is being snared 6 inches or 8 inches may be a better height. Wherever deer are around, a willow or other flexible branch should be bent over the snare. Deer may not see the noose but will certainly jump any obstacle. A knot or 'stop' on the wire of the noose will prevent it closing fully. This prevents deer or sheep getting their feet caught.

All animals caught in a snare will quickly realise struggling only tightness the noose. For this reason most catches will be taken alive if snares are checked at dawn. A stop on the snare further ensures live catches. Thus the fox can be humanely despatched by a single close up rifle shot.

Driving

So much for the snaring of individual foxes. Snaring is more often used as a general control method for reducing fox numbers in a given area. The other main method for achieving a general reduction is fox driving. This is frequently used where extensive forestry plantings harbour growing numbers of foxes, frequently in upland areas where predation of lambs is common. Twenty or so local farm folk, gamekeepers and other shotgun owners are divided into two groups, the walking and standing guns. One group lines out at each end of the woodland and, while one waits, the other line slowly walks the wood through towards them. The walking guns may have a fleeting chance at a fox but it is the standing guns who will see most of the action. These standing guns should keep quiet and still and should only shoot backwards, i.e. once foxes have run through the line. This is especially important when the walking line is drawing near. Where the woodland is too dense for the walking line to carry guns safely, they must simply beat it through as well as possible to force the foxes forward. Many regular fox drives use a few dogs, often terriers, beagles, spaniels or foxhounds. Dogs, thick cover and guns are a dangerous mixture of course. If dogs are to be used on fox drives the men must be extremely steady and reliable. Safety must come first and foremost. No amount of lambs or game saved will pay for accidents to men or dogs. Fox drives are normally carried out during winter when there is least cover and most foxes.

Digging

'Doing the dens' is an annual springtime method of taking foxes when they are at their most vulnerable. Some pseudo-naturalists fondly imagine foxes live in dens all year. The truth is they prefer heavy cover, even that afforded by dense crops like kale. Foxes only really use the dens to escape danger or to rear their young, though unseasonal hard weather can also see the dens in use. However to be sure of finding foxes in the majority of earths, terriermen traditionally 'do the dens' in spring. This springtime assault on all local dens is mainly employed in hill areas and coincides with the lambing time. Hill foxes have a harder life than their lowground cousins and are more prone to lamb killing, especially when rearing hungry litters. Personally, I am rarely in favour of controlling any mammals or birds during their breeding season. If it must be done, as in this case to prevent losses of lambs, there is a moral obligation to ensure no cubs are left orphaned. It is an unfortunate fact of life that most fox damage occurs during the fox's breeding season. The job of a working terrier is to enter the earth and face up the fox at close quarters but not to tackle it. The job of the terrier men is to dig into the earth, guided by the terrier's baying. This they will do after a short wait with shotguns, lurchers and purse nets at the ready for any bolts. Even as the digging goes on there should be a man with a shotgun on a vantage point to cover all escape routes. Naturally, terrier work is a very effective means of fox control but is not without it's problems. On hill ground, foxes are adept at finding lairs in rock fissures and other undiggable spots. In other words, the foxes are quite safe if they don't bolt. In areas where rock holes are commonplace, many terriermen prefer strong hardy terriers which are more than capable of killing foxes very quickly. The men who carry out terrier work around the high dens in spring are in the main very experienced and practical hill shepherds, gamekeepers and stalkers.

'If found roond here at lambin time a fox den is in use,

Word quickly finds by phone or van each herd an 'keeper's hoose.

Within the 'oor on banes sae bare, an' sand, an' fur, an' feather,

A shepherd and a terrier stare and shortly ithers gether'. Believe me they know their dens, their foxes and their terriers. In lesser hands this method of fox control might be open to question but so long as it is carried out by skilled local countrymen it remains a highly efficient means of protection for lambs, game and wildlife.

Gassing

Gassing is another method employed when foxes are using the dens. The powder or tablet is placed into each hole, before sealing all entrances. Reaction with the soil's dampness produces a lethal gas which kills the occupants. Of course, it is difficult to know whether vixen, dog and cubs are all at home at the time (a most unlikely event). During terrier work if it is thought either of the adults has not been accounted for the approaches to the den will be watched overnight by riflemen if the damage being done warrants it. When gassing there is no opportunity to tell whether this is necessary. However, gassing is a very simple method requiring no skill other than the ability to differentiate between fox holes and badger holes. Having diagnosed a fresh fox hole an educated guess is also needed as to when the whole family will be at home. (Mid-day during bad weather is a good time but beware of using gassing powder in windy conditions.) Gassing can of course never be carried out by a man on his own.

Moving

Moving, or more precisely moving foxes to a rifle, is a job easily carried out by two men where conifer plantations, bracken or other blocks of cover are known to conceal a fox or two but no dens. The man with the rifle (.222 or heavier) waits at a downwind vantage point overlooking an open expanse while the other man, and perhaps a dog or two, starts upwind and walks the cover through. Any resident foxes scenting or hearing of his approach will slip off downwind. If the walking man has taken his time and not unduly alarmed the fox, the rifleman should be presented with a fairly straight forward shot as his target sneaks silently off over the open towards the nearest cover.

Calling

Finally, a favourite method of fox control is calling to the gun at night. The gun used might be a .22, a .22 hornet, a .222, .243 or heavier rifle or even a 12-bore shotgun with heavy ammunition. The call used might be a small reeded wind instrument bought at the local gunshop. It is just as likely to be a couple of small tin strips taped together with a tape reed between. Foxes can even be called by people sucking through pursed lips, blowing or sucking on the back of a hand etc. etc. The object of the exercise is to produce a squeal like a stricken rabbit. This any fox within earshot will come to investigate in hopes of finding an easy meal. Some fox hunters can even imitate the various barks and yelps of dog foxes and vixens. Besides the call and the rifle, a spotlight is needed as calling is always used at night when foxes are out hunting. This is a method which can be done alone, as I usually do, but is easier done with one man working the call and lamp, and the other man the rifle. At all times they must work into the wind. This is especially important if a vermin dog is being used. The job of the dog is to apprehend the fox in the unusual event of the shot failing to stop it. This ensures that no injured fox is left to suffer. As always the object is to ensure that when culling is unavoidable it is done as quickly and humanely as possible with no chance of injured foxes being left. In practice most called foxes approach cautiously, with frequent stops which allow ample time for a well placed killing shot. In conclusion I reiterate that fox control is only morally acceptable where the damage being done can be prevented in no other way. Many other aspects of pest control can be carried out by the layman but fox control is best left to experienced hands.

12

Feral Cats

Feral cats are ordinary domestic moggies turned wild. Though feral cats are largely an urban phenomenon, this chapter concerns only rural cats. Cats take to the stray life with remarkable ease. Most cat owners who turn their charges out overnight have no idea of what cats get up to when left to their own devices, or indeed how far they travel. The truth of the matter is they range far and wide, can hunt as well as any fox or genuine Scottish wildcat, and cause considerable damage to wildlife and domestic animals and birds. Unless they are in the habit of taking kills home, their owners will be totally unsuspecting. And those are the cats who have a home to go to. Cats bred in the wild are second only to the fox in destructive qualities and some place them above that villain in the league of killers. Bred in derelict barn, beneath garden shed, in straw stack or dense woodland, they cause problems for all sorts of country folk. Gamekeepers, pigeon fanciers, rabbit catchers, poultry breeders, aviarists, gardeners, pigbreeders, cattlemen and other stockmen, all have reason to curse the wild bred cat from time to time. The verminman encounters feral cats in two ways. Firstly he may be called in by a customer to deal with a colony of them, or the flea infestation they cause. Secondly, he may be troubled with cats himself when they interfere with catches in rabbit snares or in cage traps set for pigeon, squirrel, rat and crows.

Speaking personally, I am frequently asked to do something about population explosions among feral cats. Only once have I ever been consulted about dogs (distressing cattle). As a lifelong dog owner I take strong exception to the anti-dog lobby, dog licensing and all associated hullaballoo. Cats, like sealpups, have baby faces and as such are one of the animals which laymen (particularly lay-ladies) will not hear a word against. Certainly pet cats give enormous company and pleasure to a great many people. It must, however, be realised by each cat owner that any cat allowed outdoors for long, unsupervised periods will cause inconvenience and even expense to several people within two or three miles distance.

Turning pet cats out by night is no different to the person who turns his dog out while he is away at work each day. There is, in fact, no reason why cats cannot be brought up as household pets. Many urban cats, particularly pedigreed ones, use an indoor litter tray and are never out of the house unless

25 *Feral cats.*

in a proper cat carrying box. These cats are invariably well looked after, enjoy their lives to the full, give affection and company to their owners and more importantly, do not cause any problems to other people. Cats are the only pet I can think of which live half of their lives outside the control of their owner. Like it or not, cats are pets while in the house and pests when at large.

The verminman must always work totally within the law. He must ignore people being plagued by cats who make pleas for a 'strong trap or a lethal poison'. Such requests are commonplace and the pester must play the diplomat and walk the middle line between cat haters and cat lovers. If there is any possibility at all that a troublesome cat belongs to someone it must be taken alive and every possible effort made to trace the owner. If, however, problem cats are known to be stray or wildbred there are various options within the law to deal with them. Such cats are invariably good mousers and the caring verminman will always enquire of his farming customers whether such an animal is needed. It is of course, always wise to insist the farmer pays for having the cat neutered or dressed if he wants it. This ensures that the farm to which it is taken will not become overrun with cats. It also ensures the cat is seen by a vet, as most feral cats have parasites or cat flu etc. So, cage trapping, neutering and housing in a farm (never in a house) is an effective way of turning the problem to some good. However, there are often just too many feral cats to use this solution. In such circumstances, they can be cage trapped and transported to a vet or animal protection body for a humane lethal injection. It is perfectly legal for the pester to put down caged cats himself, so long as a legal method is used. However, it goes without saying that cats are an emotive subject and, in general, the customer, the public and the protectionists are happier if a vet is involved. Nothing slower than a lethal barbiturate injection should be considered in my view. If the vet or protection group use gas or chloroform chambers or any other slow method I am sure the interests of the animals are better served if the pester destroys them himself by an accurate rifle shot. Shooting of feral cats is perfectly legal and being instantaneous is more humane than even a killing injection. Strangely, although shooting is undoubtedly the best method it is not used a lot, as modern public opinion has the brainwashed attitude that 'humane' death by gas or chloroform is quite acceptable. Shooting on the other hand is looked upon as being barbaric. That it is not even felt by the cat matters not to such people.

There will always be cat rescue societies willing to accept any cat rather than let it be put down. These societies are useful for solving the problem of small kittens or strays which have been pets at some time but any feral kittens or cats beyond the age when litters become independent of the nest cannot be considered suitable for fostering. They may look appealing but it has to be realised these are wild animals and cannot be handled.

Being a naturalist and a person interested in all animals, domestic or wild, I find it very sad that cats should need controlling at all. Surely all this anti-dog hysteria which goes on would be far better channelled into the provision of stricter controls over cat ownership, so that these intelligent and appealing animals did not have to be killed due to the thoughtlessness and ignorance of certain so-called cat lovers who allow their wards to run free, breed indiscriminately and disappear to have their litters away from home. All responsible cat owners already recommend keeping cats indoors at all times and having them neutered as a matter of course. Cat owners who object to cats being considered as pests should attempt to put their own house in order.

So much for the politics of feral cat control. The actual techniques are much less complicated. Cat cage traps vary, but all work on the same basic principle. The door is held up by a trigger which is connected to a floor pedal or bait hook well within the cage. The bait must be far enough in to ensure even the largest tom cat is fully in the cage before the door falls behind him. Normal cat cage dimensions are four feet long by eleven inches square at each end. They are easily home made. The bait being at the opposite end to the door results in cats trying to get in at the wrong end. If the mesh of the grille is too large they will reach in and attempt to paw the bait out through the wire. This can result in the trap being sprung before any cat enters. To counter this it is sensible to site two cages side by side and 'head to toe' so there is a door and bait at each end. This way they have no trouble finding the doors. Of course, the two cages must not actually be touching or a cat rattling around in one will set off the other.

Unlike some pet cats, ferals are not at all fussy and are drawn to any flesh or fish bait or tinned cat food. Milk is a very good draw but should not be used as the caught cats get covered in it and look bedraggled when taken to the vet to be put to sleep: this is even worse if a pet cat is caught and is being returned to its owner.

Of course, the type of cage described is a single catch unit only, being capable of taking one cat at a time. Multi-catchers are available and consist of larger cages which are left open. Pre-baited at a certain time each day, the object is to accustom the entire litter or small colony to enter and feed together at that time. When this is accomplished the pester will trigger the trap from a distance using a long string from his van or a nearby window. Remote control gadgets are even available on multi-catchers but the lesser extent of feral cat problems outside towns makes them impractical for the rural verminman.

13

Mustelids

The mustelids or weasel tribe are predators supreme. As well as being enemies of domestic poultry and game, they take a constant toll of all manner of wildlife. Therefore, their control is desirable in the interests of conservation. In order of size, the troublesome family members are weasel (8 inch), stoat (11 inch), mink (15 inch) (lengths do not include tails). All will kill any prey they can master, and frequently, among penned fowl, more birds than they could possibly use for food. Moreover, the mink is semi-aquatic and seldom found far from waterways. Because of this rather constricted distribution the mink tends to decimate all wildlife populations along water edges, e.g. coots, moorhens, watervoles, wild duck, frogs, songbirds and fish. Because mink follow waterways, they have no trouble in finding one another. For this reason a handful of individuals is enough to colonise a wide area. Unlike that foreign alien the mink, the stoat and weasel only require control, certainly not eradication. Of course, where an individual, a pair, or a family group is raiding pigeon loft, hen house, aviary or game pen *all* those guilty must be apprehended.

Weasel

Being designed with the narrow burrows of mouse, vole and mole in mind, the tiny weasel is far less of a pest than its two larger cousins. Nor can it climb half as well as they do. It is more or less confined to ground level prey. Sometimes it will scramble into a thick hedge to raid a songbird's nest but that's about as agile as a weasel can be. Being so small it may easily enter small cracks in timber stock enclosures so long as not too much climbing is involved. I remember the aftermath of a weasel attack upon an aviary full of valuable show canaries. Four of the lovely Border canaries had been left, heads missing, in their cage corners. Everyone is familiar with the extremely narrow spacing of the wire grills used for cage birds. Only weasels can squeeze through aviary wires. Further weasel evidence was the fact that only those cages on the lower tier had been entered, the culprit being unable to climb any higher.

26   *Mink shot while swimming.*

27   *Bitch weasel: tiny, but will kill prey much larger than itself.*

Young chicks, ducklings and other prey unable to get off the ground are very vulnerable to weasel attack, the predators often gaining access to their compounds via underground mole runs. The eggs of ground-nesting birds, domestic or wild, are a favourite meal of the weasel.

As with all mustelids, males are generally larger than females and it is my belief that weasel attacks on adult poultry, pet rabbits and the like are most often attributable to males.

Stoat

Of the trio, the stoat is the one most commonly in trouble with the vermin catcher. I have known him caught in traps set in cottage roofs for rat. Most countrymen have at some time witnessed a stoat effortlessly climbing a tree. It goes without saying therefore, that the stoat who knows where a dinner lives will most likely be able to gain access. Much larger than the weasel, he is nonetheless, slim enough to wriggle through some very small spaces; an inch is more than enough. Once inside he is lightning quick and not at all disadantaged by darkness. This and his climbing ability makes him the very devil among penned birds or small pet animals etc. In any area where uncommon small animals or birds have a foothold, the stoat should be strictly controlled. There is no place for him on such places as nature reserves. Some modern day protectionists, not countrymen I hasten to add, find themselves running nature reserves and adopt the attitude that any area protected from 'man' will look after itself. The point is that stoats, can be seen anywhere; terns, avocets, stints and other vulnerable species cannot. If it means killing a few common animals until some uncommon ones become common again, so be it. Nothing saddens me more than an ignorance of basic wildlife management among those who hold our heritage in trust.

Mink

The mink is reviled just as much as the rat. Of all pests they are the only two upon which all-out war is waged. Like the rat the American mink is an illegal immigrant, a foreign interloper, an alien. Like the rat, the mink is proving unstoppable. Like the rat, it is hard to find anything good to say about the mink. Originally established in the wild after escaping from fur farms, this animal encountered no natural enemy in the UK. Its spread has been phenomenal (not of course without assistance from the lunatic fringe who go around 'liberating' them on an unsuspecting countryside). It is sad to say that, had no mink ever escaped from fur farms, the feral mink would be a menace in Britain today entirely through the efforts of various 'animal rights groups'! How true it is that man is the most guilty 'pest' on this planet.

Anyway, returning to furred vermin, Mr Mink, despite being bigger and heavier than the stoat, is almost as good a climber when it comes to breaching the security of hen house, pigeon loft or even turkey pen. His bulk also works in his favour if an entry hole is not quite wide enough. A few minutes' work with tooth and claw will normally force entry. Terrific numbers of poultry may be lost to one mink in one night's work – the most I have heard of was thirty. He will always kill until his stamina or bloodlust run out, which means he usually kills them all. I don't believe he necessarily has more bloodlust than the other two mustelids but he certainly has more staying power when the feathers start flying!

As with the weasel and stoat, he is not only a threat to confined quarry. Unlike the weasel and stoat, our wildlife has evolved no resistance to the mink's depredations. I believe, as with the rat, there will quickly come a time when no county in Britain is without wild mink. We have reached the point when it is too late to deport him. He has now become a resident and we can only do our best to restrict his harm to a minimum. Having looked at the species let us now consider control methods.

Tunnel Trapping

Controlling stoats and weasels on wildlife reserves and game preserves, is done by maintaining a network of Fenn Mk IV traps in small tunnels. The first thing such a trap line illustrates is just how abundant stoats and weasels really are and just how inconspicuous they are until trapped.

The old style of tunnel trap, popular since gin trapping, is a single ended affair with a bait between trap and closed end. Open-ended tunnels, my own preference, require no bait whatsoever. They rely upon the knowledge of the trapper to site them where stoats and weasels will find them. The light at the end of the tunnel is enough of a bait. Mustelids can never resist investigating a hole, burrow, pipe, bower or tunnel. The same tunnels of wood, stones, turfs etc. can be used for mink but the larger Mk VI or the Juby is more suitable in mink tunnels.

Cage trapping

Cage traps are very popular for mink. Mink in this country are all escapees or descendants of escapees from fur farms. Naturally, fur farmers use cage traps to recapture any lost mink alive. When mink first became a problem in the wild it was to mink farmers that people turned for advice. So the fur farm method of using cage traps became the main means of control for feral mink. Cage traps are, of course, large and bulky. They require regular baiting, camouflaging against the public and they present the trapper with the problem of having to kill the captives.

I always like to have cage traps handy for odd jobs, especially squirrels and feral cats, but I have to admit they have nothing of the all-round usefulness of spring traps. However, let me detail the best baits for cage trapping mustelids.

For mink any sort of freshwater fish, eels or fish offal has the greatest pulling power, but fresh rabbit flesh or offal is just as good. A reader's letter to *Shooting News* came from a Cumbrian trapper who used pieces of kipper. Being cured, this bait did not go off in hot weather, nor did it attract bluebottles, and we can all testify to the aromatic qualities of kippers! All mustelids may be drawn to fresh rabbit, rabbit paunches or any other raw meat, tinned cat or dog meat, or a few spots of blood which your friendly neighbourhood butcher may fill into a small bottle for you. Most attractive of all is the musk or urine of a previous catch. The skunk-like musk glands of all mustelids are in the genital region. By wiping the trap plate with the scent gland of a kill, especially a female, the trap is made irresistable to any other mustelid passerby. Of course, these baits work just as well in cul de sac tunnels as in cages. To many trappers the thought of a baitless trap is inconceivable; tradition has decreed that. All I say is that in my own experience precautionary traps need no baiting. By precautionary I mean traps not set for a particular individual. Where I sometimes do bait spring traps is when dealing with one or two particular raiders known to be returning to a pen of birds. Live birds are a great attraction and a good fresh bait may be necessary to compete with such a draw. Indeed if the birds can be housed elsewhere it is a good idea to remove them leaving only one of the mustelid's previous kills. It goes without saying this kill is used to bait the tunnel or cage trap.

Shooting and Dogging

There is another sure draw for the weasel clan but it is not a bait. When a hunting mustelid is chanced upon it is very simple to call the animal very close by pursing your lips and drawing in air to produce a high squeak like a stricken rabbit. On hearing this distress call the quarry will work its way forward until it can be shot or the dog tried at it, if you have no gun. The stoat has an incredible sprinting and jinking ability when coursed. Even if safety lies twenty yards away the stoat might well reach it. Mink in comparison are slow and easily caught by a dog. Most vermin dogs are fairly small, however, and a mink fighting for its life is a formidable foe. The correct training of vermin dogs is to start them on young rats, then adult rats, then weasel, stoat, mink all the way up the size ladder to fox. By entering the dog to its foes in order of size it is never over-matched and becomes supremely confident. Only a dog experienced on smaller fry should ever be allowed to tackle mink.

Other than 'calling', there are other opportunities to shoot or dog mustelids. These come when one is disturbed with its prey. If the pester keeps still and quiet the predator invariably returns to the scene of the crime within a few moments. It must be pointed out, of course, that 99 per cent of mustelids killed by verminmen are taken in traps. Only rarely do actual face to face encounters present themselves.

14

Crows and Gulls

Both these families are widely regarded as scavengers and foragers, but it is seldom realised the extent to which they are also predators. Dealing with the crows first, the most troublesome family members are the carrion crow and the hooded crow. The place of these two in the great scheme of things is to do away with all dead or dying animals. Unfortunately, they often include the weak and vulnerable, such as newborn lambs. If new lambs are unable to stand, they run a grave risk of losing their tongues or eyes to crows. Crows, used to tearing at sheep carrion, will just as readily fly down onto the stomach of an upturned adult sheep. (Today's fat, flat-backed sheep have the greatest difficulty in righting themselves if they topple.) The easiest way for a crow to eat from a dead adult sheep is to pierce the taut belly skin with a stab or two of his dagger like beak. The tear thus made allows the long stringy intestines to be easily drawn through. Unsavoury though it may be to say so, crows do not seem over concerned whether the sheep is dead or merely upturned. It has to be said that the heavyweight of the crow clan, the raven, shares this predilection for ewes' innards and lambs' eyes and tongues. The raven, however, is seldom numerous enough to cause such damage consistently. The carrion crow and hoodie are both abundant, the former mainly on low ground, the latter on high ground. My reason for opening this chapter in such graphic, gory detail, is to counter the wet assertion that crows only feed on the weakest, thus ensuring the survival of the fittest. It is an idea as unknowledgeable as the one about foxes only visiting lambing fields in search of stillborn lambs or afterbirths. Unlike the 'experts' who make these theories, foxes and crows do not share the Walt Disney approach to nature. I concede they eat a lot of insects, shellfish and scraps from rubbish dumps. Indeed, they are yet another creature which is a pest only outside towns, and then only in certain situations. I do not advocate nationwide war against all crows. Species and situations differ. Rooks, for example, can be beneficial at times when their flocks concentrate upon arable insect pests. Indeed, of all the troublesome crows – i.e. carrion, hooded, magpie, jackdaw, jay and rook – the rook is easily the most numerous and yet the least murderous.

All crows will take eggs at every opportunity. Carrion and hooded crows and magpies will also kill chicks and will often not even eat or carry them off.

Nests preyed upon include all species of wild and domestic duck, plovers, oystercatchers, curlews, partridges, pheasants, free range hens, terns, gulls or in fact any of our vast number of ground nesting birds and many of the remaining hedge and tree nesters. This egg and chick diet may not warrant general control of crows. However, around farmyards, game preserves, game farms and nature reserves the time to carry out crow control is before damage occurs. Crows can also be responsible for infecting domestic birds and game birds with gapeworm, the internal parasite which is responsible for that dreaded condition, the 'gapes'. Crow chicks are, of course, calling for food when all other birds have eggs or chicks. That is when the hunting crows are at their most persistent. By then it is too late to prevent enormous losses to poultry, game and wildbirds. Similarly, around lambing fields, the time to reduce carrion or hooded crow numbers is before the lambs start arriving.

Crow Control

Methods of reducing crows are much the same for all the corvid species. At the outset, I must state that poisoned eggs or carrion is not one of these methods. Shepherds and gamekeepers witnessing the disastrous effects of crow predation have been known to set such baits in desperation, and for the want of a more effective cure to their troubles. By detailing the legal alternatives here I would hope to persuade the minority who act illegally that they cause needless harm to wildlife and to the image of their professions. Leave it to vermin to threaten our wildlife. It is your job to ease the problems, not add to them. Although the lesser crows can be troublesome in certain places, it is not everywhere that jays and magpies are found. Jackdaws and rooks are fairly approachable as crows go, therefore they seldom require the cunning necessary to counter the carrion and hooded crows. It is the carrion and hoodie to which the following recommendations apply. When required, the same procedures will do for the others.

Shooting

Crows wander far and wide in winter and though they may appear numerous the customer may be inclined to ignore them unless damage occurs. By spring they should be dispersing to pair up and claim nesting territories elsewhere. It is then an eye must be kept open for any which stay around to set up home.

A makeshift hide near the chosen nest site may allow the .22 rifle to account for the pair by day. The first shot may be propped up to act as a decoy for the other. Hoodies and carrion crows tend to favour lone trees in open situations where they can spot any approaching danger or potential victim. In the few cases where cover lies close enough to hide a shotgunner, better results may ensue. Mostly the rifle is needed to make up for the difficulty of approach.

By night the .22 rifle and silencer can be used from beneath the tree. In lieu of a moon a spotlight can be used to show the birds. If a helper is available, two shotgunners can approach the nesting tree by day. In the unlikely event the birds sit tight this allows a shooter to stand at each side of the tree. (Crows will always leave by the opposite side if only one gunner approaches.) If the pair fly off before the tree is reached, it is a good idea for one to hide within gunshot of the tree while the other walks away. Crows may be intelligent when it comes to preying on the vulnerable. They are not so hot at arithmetic however, and do not realise that two approaching, minus one leaving, equals one remaining. Having accounted for the pair, keep an eye on the nest. It will probably be taken over by another pair.

Other than at the nest site, shooting may be used in conjunction with calls and decoys of various sorts. Crows do not tolerate predators in their territories. Stuffed foxes or plastic owls or a live white ferret under a small dome of chickenwire will all attract crows to be shot. Plastic crows are also available and one or two near the fox, owl or ferret, will add to the effectiveness, particularly if the gunner blows on a crow call from time to time. Any general vermin squeaker (as described for mustelids) will also bring crows to investigate the possibility of an easy meal.

Cage Trapping

Cage trapping is the only legal alternative to shooting. Crow cages are used to effect a general reduction rather than to bring certain troublesome individuals to book. Cages are, of course, more suitable for the gregarious crow species such as rooks, and jackdaws. Where lack of control has allowed a build-up of crows to the extent that previously ignored predation becomes intolerable, shooting cannot be relied upon. It is then that cage traps come into their own. Choice of bait will to some extent determine species of crow caught: maize, grain or bread for rooks and jackdaws, eggs (or golfballs), paunched rabbits or sheep carrion for hooded/carrion crows. The latter baits will avoid gamebirds being caught and subsequently killed by caught crows. Crow cages are very similar to feral pigeon cages. Indeed it is not unknown for jackdaws to be caught in pigeon cages after entering to kill captive pigeons. The only difference between pigeon and crow cages is the size of the

28   *Crow decoy, using dead crow, dead pigeon and scattered feathers.*

29   *Carrion crow and .22 rifle.*

83

30   *Decoy little owl with flapping wings to attract mobbing crows.*

funnels. For crows the ground level funnels should be 11 inches square outside tapering to 5 inches square inside. Funnels down through the roof can be used to avoid gamebird catches. Roof funnels should be 20 inches diameter tapering to 8 inches inside. A perch in the funnel entrance is also helpful. Funnels should be removable to facilitate prebaiting. As with pigeon trapping, a live decoy adds greatly to the success of the cage. When removing caught crows for humane culling a female may be left in the cage as a decoy. A drinker and some sort of shelter must be provided for it, of course. The use of a live carrion/hooded decoy further adds to the selective attraction of that species as opposed to the less malicious crows. Of these less troublesome and more gregarious crow species it has to be said they are far less suspicious of cage trapping and therefore far easier to cage trap than the sly carrion/hooded crows which more often warrant control. For more details on cage trapping see under feral pigeons, as the procedures are more or less the same for either type of pest.

Gulls

Among that family commonly referred to as 'seagulls' there are five common British species i.e. black headed, common, greater and lesser black backed and the herring gull. It is the black backed and herring which may interest the pester from time to time.

All species of gulls have increased their numbers dramatically over recent years, due to their adaptability to man's wastefulness. In fact many so-called 'seagulls' rarely if ever see the sea nowadays.

Massive rubbish tips on city outskirts provide rich pickings; large undisturbed reservoirs provide safe roosting out on their open waters. Gulls are blamed for carrying diseases from the dumps to our reservoirs and elsewhere. There is also the charge that enormous flocks of gulls roosting on reservoirs cause considerable pollution of our drinking water supplies with their droppings. Having over-populated available nest sites a new phenomenon of gulls treating buildings as nesting cliffs causes problems of fouling and flies.

Even on traditional nesting sites such as offshore islands, the increase in gulls, particularly herring gulls, has meant unbalanced predation upon less common seabirds such as puffins and terns. This explosion of gull numbers and the resultant decrease in auk and tern numbers has been so serious as to force various naturalist groups to actively pursue programmes of gull culling. As one who is often exasperated by my fellow naturalists' inability to understand the occasional need for a certain amount of 'wildlife management', I could use no better example of the seriousness of gull overpopulation and predation.

The herring gull and lesser black back are very closely related and, apart from colour are almost identical. Both are equally voracious. The greater black backed gull, the giant of the family, is an enormous bird with an appetite to match.

All three species are very argumentative, even within their own nesting colonies. They think nothing of a spot of cannibalism if a careless neighbour leaves an egg or chick unguarded for a second. Needless to say, any smaller seabirds such as shearwaters, are in grave danger of being eaten, even the adults. Amazingly, gulls tend to swallow their prey whole if it is at all possible. Failure to do so will result in the prize being stolen by another gull. Excavator drivers on rubbish tips have seen them kill rats and swallow them whole! They will quickly learn where salmon are struggling over shallows on their annual upstream race. Lambs and red deer calves fall easy victim to them, as do upturned sheep.

Ground nesting birds, including gamebirds and domestic fowl frequently lose their eggs and chicks to these gulls. Indeed, if the incubating hen is brave enough to resist or silly enough to hang around, she too will fall victim.

The great black backed in particular can be likened to the pike – the 'shark' of British freshwater. Just as pike have been caught and found to contain whole ducks in their stomachs, whole bantams, pigeons and part grown hares, rabbits and game birds have been found in culled great blackbacks.

Gull problems as described on reservoirs and dumps are usually dealt with by the local authority or the Ministry of Agriculture, using repelling or dispersal techniques. When gulls have to be controlled in the interests of less harmful seabirds, the work is generally done by a government department or bird protection body. Seldom is the pester involved.

Where the pester may find his services required is in the protection of stocks of sheep, deer and game on coastal estates, especially if either of the three predatory gulls have breeding sites within a few miles. Unfortunately, cage trapping is ineffective when it comes to gulls. This only leaves shooting, which means the shotgunner or rifleman must establish the times of day gull damage is being done. By setting an attractive bait such as a paunched rabbit or two near a natural hide, it should be possible to account for the miscreants. Shot birds may be propped up as decoys to look as if they are feeding at the bait. Hunting gulls can spot feeding gulls from a great distance and will invariably come in for a closer look.

As with all pest problems where it may be found that no legal remedy proves effective, it is worthwhile making approaches to the Nature Conservancy Council and the Ministry of Agriculture pest control division. There are certain instances where special licences may be issued for the culling of protected species or for the use of strictly controlled methods such as narcotised baits.

15

Deer

The great estates of the Highlands and other hill areas of Britain hold our population of red deer in trust and generally do a very good job of protecting them for us. The same can also be said of the fallow deer, the sheepish animal of the famous English Parks. Both species are professionally managed by full time stalkers, wardens and rangers. Both are relatively easily managed herd animals, unlike the roe deer. It is really the secretive little woodland roe deer which concerns the pester in as much as it occurs almost everywhere there are well wooded country landscapes, and in many places where no one is employed or qualified to look after them.

It is with certain misgivings I include a deer chapter at all in a pest control book. I would have included them in the Near Pest and Non-Pest Chapter but the subject deserves space of its own.

During my days as a beatkeeper, shotgun drives were still used as an acceptable means of roe deer control. It was a method I found very unsavoury. That was towards the end of the bad old days when deer were still looked upon as pests. Earlier escapes from parks and estates and massive post war conifer afforestation had led to an unprecedented spread of deer into counties and areas where they had previously been uncommon or unknown. This new distribution was, of course, accompanied by damage to crops and trees. Deer became regarded as pests and the traditional country weapon, the shotgun, was used in the way it was for hares and foxes: deer drives became common. Drives were not very effective and caused enough disturbance to further accelerate the distribution of deer.

All that has thankfully changed. Deer have come to be looked upon as an asset by landowners, estates, forestry concerns and farmers. This asset requires management, of course, as do all assets.

Management or rifle 'culling' of deer is quite simply an exercise in maintaining their numbers at a level the habitat can support. Culling may be carried out for two reasons: to prevent damage or to provide revenue from the sale of trophy stalking to visiting sportsmen. Whichever is the aim, the means is always the same, i.e. numbers are kept at a level which promotes health and well-being of both the deer and their habitat: each being reliant upon the other. It was long thought that trophy production was best served by culling all bucks with poor 'heads' (antlers). Nowadays it is realised that the quality of the trophy can vary on an individual male from year to year, mainly dependent upon the quality of his territory and the feeding it produces. By keeping stocks at a reasonable number both aims of management are served: heads will improve and damage will decline.

'Deer Damage' is due mainly to the cosmopolitan diet of the roe deer but is also caused by 'fraying' of saplings by the bucks' horns. Fraying is part of the buck's territory-marking habit and also occurs in his attempts to rid his horns of their winter velvet in the spring. Frayed saplings are instantly recognisable. Attacked trees are normally an inch to three inches in diameter. Their leaves are frequently withered, while all around are lush. The bark of the trunk between eight and eighteen inches from the ground is hopelessly shredded and hoof scrapes radiate out over the ground around the roots. These scrapes are caused by his bull-like stamping and pawing as he thrashes the trunk with his horns.

As regards damage by grazing and browsing, evidence manifests itself on all types of valuable vegetation. Most noticeable among these are newly planted trees which are lamentably vulnerable to browsing deer when lying snow covers all but the tops. Similarly, young trees can go ignored by deer until weeding makes them stand out. Browsing may then occur. In either case, the removal of the tree tip results in trees growing in tuning fork shape instead of straight and useable. Severe browsing can cause a young tree to grow into nothing more than a bushy shrub. In woodland, which is hopelessly overpopulated by deer a 'browse line' develops at head height to the deer. Very little leaf or cover survives below this line. Browse lines are particularly noticeable when viewing the outside of the wood from a distance. Denuding of this severity is, of course, very bad for the deer, the habitat and the woodland game and wildlife. There is also the damage, mainly nocturnal, which occurs among the crops outside the forestry. Very young wheat and barley, kale, carrots, turnips and other root crops are particularly vulnerable. Damage to crops is often a bone of contention in these days when woodland is treated as speculative property and is frequently not under the same ownership as the fields. The woodland owner often finds himself under pressure from neighbouring farmers to do something about deer damage to crops.

Now that the shotgun is frowned upon for use against deer, their management has become a far more humane affair. They are now protected by close seasons and are no longer pursued by bands of farmers and others hoping to pay for deer damage in the sale of venison. Today's deer stalker works alone. He must be as quiet and unobtrusive in the woods as the deer themselves. His weapon is a heavy calibre rifle fitted with a powerful telescopic sight. Only stationary or very slow moving nearby deer are shot, the single bullet being accurately aimed at the heart (or very occasionally the neck vertebrae or, if from behind, the back of the head). No natural death is

31   A deluxe high seat for roe control.

32   Fire breaks in spruce plantations assist roe control. Massive increases in upland afforestation is responsible for roe colonisation of many new areas.

as quick and clean. Nor for that matter the all too common deaths on the roads or at the hands of poachers. Of course, no matter how accurately shot, a deer may occasionally run for several seconds before falling. In the heavy cover which roe deer prefer, this necessitates a good deer dog. Such a dog must stay strictly by the stalker, quiet and attentive and should only move after the shot, and then only if told to. Of all aspects of dog work, deer stalking is perhaps the most demanding in obedience and steadiness. In practice, for every dozen stalkers there is only one who has a dog. It is to him the others go when trouble arises. Even after this time lapse, a good deer dog will lead the men to the carcase; and that despite the inevitable stamping and searching around which has preceded his summoning.

As if the foregoing account of rifle stalking isn't difficult enough that is only half of the story. It is not just a case of the stalker shooting any deer he comes across. During winter only females or 'does' are in season, during summer only bucks. It is a generally accepted principle of roe control that the winter cull, i.e. the doe cull, is the one which should bring about the desired reduction. During the buck season only yearlings (i.e. bucks born the previous summer) or very old bucks should make up the cull. This avoids the removal of dominant bucks holding territory. A territory suddenly becoming vacant during the rut will cause much squabbling among lesser bucks and a resultant increase in territorial fraying. Mind you, if numbers are high and a large cull is required, it can be a good idea to shoot any buck holding a sparse or easily shot territory. His removal will result in an influx of lesser rivals which can then be stalked over a period of days. The same applies to dominant does in winter.

The ins and outs of roe stalking could easily fill an entire book however, and often have done. All I propose to do here is outline the general methods and alternatives. Other than stalking these involve Calling, Moving and High Seats.

'Calling'

Calling of roe deer is a well developed art on the continent yet still in its infancy here. It is a method of the highly skilled specialist, not the pester of all trades. Such specialised advice on calling, and all other matters of deer control for that matter, is readily available from the British Deer Society or the Game Conservancy.

'Moving'

Moving requires at least two men. It is a method I described in detail when dealing with foxes and involves the rifleman lying in wait at a downwind clearing while his companion and dog slowly walks the deer towards him.

'Slowly' is the operative word, the rifleman requiring time to age and sex each deer before deciding to shoot or not.

High Seats

The idea of high seats is to provide the rifleman with an elevated hide in the woodland which will take his scent well over the deers' heads and will, of course, give him the ideal situation for studying and selecting which deer to cull. Of course, it is quite possible to sit for hours in a high seat and never see a deer. Their proper sighting is vital and even then it is often more profitable to climb down and recommence stalking on foot. Like all methods, high seats have their place, though I feel their usefulness can be overrated at times.

All the foregoing has concerned the prevention of damage by the shooting of deer. Various alternatives are available but most involve the initial planning of the forestry even before the planting stage: the more scrub and undergrowth available, the less deer will trouble trees. Vulnerable young trees should not, where possible, be planted near thicket edges (from which deer will emerge to eat them!) It is just asking for trouble to plant saplings on known favourite areas of deer within woods. Certain species of trees are less attractive to deer than others. The timing of planting should coincide with times of least deer damage. Details of these planning schemes, and many more, are available to landowners from knowledgeable stalkers or from the organisations already mentioned.

Where it is too late to make changes in the woodland there are, of course, various repellant tree guards, sprays, pastes and the like which can minimise damage. However, no amount of forest planning or repellants will do away with the obligation to properly manage deer stocks where they exist. It is a job which needs a special skill and should not be entrusted to any Tom, Dick or Harry simply because they own a rifle of sufficient calibre.

16

Moles

As often as not the mole is named moudie, moudiewarp, moldywarp or suchlike, depending on your local tongue. In mine he sometimes gets moudie but so does the water vole, or water moudie, as we say. Indeed I even know a local lad nicknamed Moudie on account of him being a miner. So it would seem that anything or anyone prone to burrowing might be labelled Moudie hereabouts.

He has other names which can't be mentioned. These are the ones I hear him referred to by irate customers: particularly when Moudie has come along just after the sowing of a cereal crop, the laying of a new lawn or golf green, the raking of a driveway, the transferal of bedding plants etc. In all cases Moudie is not the problem. It is his attempts at landscape gardening which find objection. Home cures? You wouldn't believe the sights which welcome me on mole jobs. Home cures nine times out of ten serve no purpose other than to make life difficult for the moudieman who has to repair the mess made by the customer as well as the moles. Lawns with half buried bottles sprouting out strike me as being no improvement upon those with mole heaves. Apparently the wind whistling in the bottles is enough to start a subterranean lemming-like stampede for pastures new. Pity the moles don't know the theory! Shotgun wounds here and there across the lawn tell of the 'acoustic' approach having failed. I would guess this action is designed to frighten the little beggars to death and, of course, to vent some of the host's frustration. It is not one of my usual methods, but I have shot moles. Here is how. Go out to a heavily infested field three or four hours after a heavy snowfall. All fresh heaves are then starkly obvious, the rest being under the snow. Making sure no one is looking, load the shotgun and, on tiptoe, stalk slowly towards each mound keeping a sharp eye out for the slightest movement of soil. When a heave is seen to heave take aim from a few feet, and on the next upward shove – fire! Scoop away what remains of the heave, and there is your mole spotted with red droplets over his perforated velvet pelt.

Other home non-cures include mole smokes shoved into the tunnels. In the absence of the real thing, moth balls, paraffin, creosote, petrol, those pieces of 'coconut tablet' to be seen in public urinals, or Jeyes fluid, will apparently suffice. (I wonder if Messrs Jeyes are aware that their fluid is a world renowned repellent poured out liberally around the coutryside to get rid of every manner of creepy-crawly, rodent, fox or any other creature credited with the sense of smell.) If you are one who has invested heavily in any of the foregoing, let me gently break the news. It don't work! Here is why. Beneath that array of mounds is a network of horizontal tunnels with compacted sides. They are Moudie's worm traps. Enjoying a snooze for four hours or so to let them fill, he then comes shuffling along gobbling the trapped worms as he goes for four hours or so, which includes a bit of new shovelling, before going back to bed for another four hours to sleep it all off. (I know some humans like that, though they can't work the same.) Remembering the excavations are the problem, not the mole: it is senseless to contaminate his feeding runs with so called repellants. They don't kill him but force him to build new tunnels alongside to provide his next meal. Repelling therefore, results in double the number of mounds. I can only say one thing in favour of mole smokes. They are handy for bolting rats if you've forgotten the ferret! Never use them to bolt laid up ferrets as most contain a poison and your ferret cannot push up a soil plug between himself and the approaching fumes, as Moudie does expertly.

I have known farm dogs which frequently caught moles by approaching a hill in the making, and striking with a frenzy of digging claws just at the right moment to have him out. Some country cats catch them when they venture into daylight. A local paper carries a weekly nature feature in which the author once noted, as had I, the numerous molehills in the central grass verge of a nearby dual carriageway. What surprised me was the way he stated they *must* have got there by burrowing. It seems he had no experience of moles being killed on roads or moles being met with feeding on the surface among grasses etc. Both are common sights to the outdoorsman and rather gave away his poor credentials regarding such writing.

The numerous injured kestrels and owls in my care over the years have all relished moles from my traps. So it is to be assumed moles foraging on top, run a considerable risk. Like shrews they are very fierce with one another outside their spring breeding season. Indeed any mole met with on top should only be lifted by the tail as their stumpy bodies belie their agile wriggling and finger-nipping abilities. Their tiny needle-like teeth are like those of other insectivores i.e. shrews, bats and hedgehogs. Also like hedgehogs, they are much faster than they look both above and below ground. And another similarity to Hedgie is the number of fleas they carry. Or is it just that neither has a coat able to conceal fleas? The largest fleas I know of are those found on moles – dark brown, long and springy. I have seen them almost a quarter inch in length! One learner to whom I was trying to show them stood yards away in terror. Needless to say he never made the grade!

In small gardens, regardless of the number of hills, there is invariably just

33 About as much as most folk will ever see of "Molie".

34 Half barrel mole trap prior to lightly covering with soil.

one mole. Having been called to a garden mole job, planted a trap or two and returned next day to remove the rascal, it always amuses me to hear the customer exclaim 'Is that all the size it is'! For weeks they have been the losers in a battle of wits. Seeing just one puny mole, not quarter the size expected, they can't believe he alone is guilty of causing such earth shattering upheaval.

So much for Moudie madness, such is the effect moles have upon folk. In truth the mole is a podgy little animal resembling a velvety black pudding (the little chip shop variety, not the big butchers' window type). A black pudding with feet, what's more, no legs – just feet. He also has a pokey nose and a tiny tail but that's about all. Eyes and ears are all but invisible. Two things make moles easy to kill – they are very active and very greedy. Thus they lend themselves to trapping or poisoning. Personally, I prefer to trap small moles jobs such as gardens and poison the larger agricultural jobs.

Mole Trapping

To trap a mole one needs a mole trap. The professionals choice is the tongs or pincer type of implement which is planted head down with its legs in the air. There are other mole traps on the market but the only other serious contender is the half-barrel or Duffus trap. It is worth having a few of these where public access is a problem, as they are very difficult to see when set in a run. My main objection to them is their length and therefore the amount of the burrow which has to be opened out to receive them. Mole tunnels have numerous twists, turns and junctions. It is normally possible, by using the probe, to detect a straight section of tunnel to be opened by spade or trowel to take the trap. However, even then it is not uncommon to break into the run and find an unexpected junction. The short jaws of a pincer trap can normally still be fitted but the longer Duffus presents a problem. I also feel it takes less effort for a mole to trigger the pincer type. Imagine having probed around (not near fresh hills) until you feel the sudden give which signifies a burrow. Try another few inches around this spot until another give shows the direction of the tunnel. Now lay your trap jaws on the spot and mark around them with the trowel edge. Remove this tiny turf and excavate the soil below. The rod will have told you at what depth to expect the run. Clean out the run with your fingers. Remember mole tunnels have compacted sides so all loose soil must be removed and the set made as natural as possible. As with all other types of trapping there should be no unnecessary scent of tobacco, soap, dog, ferret, etc. on your fingers. I habitually rub my hands in the soil of the freshest mole hill before starting. Now, insert the trap jaws down the shaft to fit snugly into the run. All that remains is to tear the bit of turf into two or three bits with which to roof the trap jaws. Make this roof grass side up then sprinkle on some of the extra soil to seal out all draughts and light. If the site is not under grass or there is no turf available, the roofing of the trap will require two or three small flat stones before sprinkling on the soil. If no stones or other materials are handy, bits of cardboard can be torn up to roof the jaws.

Initially, the traps should be checked as often as possible. Moles are solitary beings for most of the year but when they are together it is advisable to empty and reset the traps as soon as they catch. The fresh scent of a friend or relative on the trap is very attractive to any subsequent moles which come along. (This applies to most types of trapping e.g. there may be a delay in catching the first but the rest should quickly follow.)

Worm Baiting

Poisoning moles requires worms. Poisoning lots of moles requires lots of worms! If ever you are driving along a country road and chance to spy a distant figure trudging along with a bucket in the wake of a plough, you can bet it's the local mole man gathering bait. This plough-following habit is a science in itself. Once walking on the new crumbling soil has been mastered, and the exact distance you can allow the plough to get in front before the gulls overtake you and steal your worms, it becomes an interesting pastime for its own sake. Upturned field mice and even the occasional mole may be chanced upon, as well as a varied selection of insects and grubs. What I find most fascinating are the tiny pieces of willow pattern plate and other odd bits and pieces which are often uncovered. Each one has me fondly imagining I might one day be able to give up this toil for the millionaire's vocation!

Your bucket is brimming with worms if the field has been good to you. (Fields vary enormously in their stock of worms; old grass is by far the best.) Keep them alive in moist soil and only prepare enough for a few hours ahead, lest they go off. To prepare them, simply take one by one, enough worms for the foreseeable future and run them twixt thumb tip and two finger tips, to remove all soil. Drop the clean worms into a clean container and measure on the strychnine which 'The Ministry' has seen fit to grant you.

On the job it is again a matter of finding the runs with your probe. This time no digging is needed as a baited worm is simply dropped down the probe hole using a make-shift set of tweezers. A lot of well-meaning advice is proferred regarding the best runs to bait. In practice it is enough to avoid the area of most recent upheaval and to locate and bait the runs between the older hills, preferably not too far from those newest ones. There is no need to go hunting for the runs to the mole's water supply, nor the fieldside run beneath the hedge or along the foot of a wall. If the site is near an edge then fair enough, you will find a main run there. Contrary to common belief, it is not best to bait the edges if you are working in the field centre. This advice dates back to pre-poison times when the fieldside runs were favourite trapping places.

Gassing

Gassing mole runs is done by inserting powders or tablets which react to the soil's moisture and give off a poisonous gas. In my view, mole runs are far too shallow to be gassed safely. The smell above ground makes it obvious the gas is escaping. The method, therefore, cannot be relied upon to kill moles but will certainly make them seal off their present runs and set about digging some new ones! Result? More mole hills.

17

Pigeons, Starlings and Sparrows

Woodpigeon flocks cause colossal damage to agriculture every year. Almost all crops are attractive to their cosmopolitan tastes at some time or other, especially when there is snow on the ground. Oil seed rape, that modern phenomenon which patches the summer countryside in paint box yellow, is most at risk and draws pigeons from miles around in late winter and spring. Wheat, barley, oats, peas, beans, cabbage, lettuce, cauliflower, turnip, carrots – the list is endless. That should mean the work is endless. It should, but it does not. The woodpigeon in flight is an extremely wary and sporting quarry. For that reason there are countless shooters prepared to control woodpigeons for no charge. Verminmen rarely bother with woodpigeons. Stock doves, which nest in tree holes and often associate with woodies are now protected by law, another reason why a knowledge of nature is needed by the gunner.

'Dookit Doos'

Feral pigeons, on the other hand, are not a sporting species and as such, only the humble pester is available to deal with them. More often referred to as street pigeons, squabs, dookit doos or 'those damn pigeons', they are the multi coloured, nondescript, highly successful mongrel birds to be found in every city, town, village, and farm steading in the country. The problems they cause are less to do with what they eat and more to do with where they choose to live. Being originally domesticated from the cliff nesting rock dove, they now look upon every conceivable type of building as nothing more than some rather fancy cliffs. Only the rat and house sparrow share the feral pigeon's dependence upon man. Dovecotes or 'dookits' still stand around the countryside in various states of dereliction since the days when pigeon was the only meat we could keep alive throughout winter. Crop rotation, turnips and other advances in farming allowed the dookits to become redundant. It seems the pigeons don't know that, however, as they are still there today, despite fallen roofs and cracked walls. Where this accommodation has

35 *One of over seventy 'Dookits' still standing in East Lothian.*

36 *Almost 150 feral pigeons in a multicatcher on a granary roof.*

collapsed altogether the birds have simply moved into the nearest farm steading. Considering a great many dookits were built in the steading anyway, it is no small wonder almost every farm now has a colony of feral pigeons living in and upon its buildings.

Roosts

Feral pigeons are creatures of habit. Each individual will roost on exactly the same spot on exactly the same roof timber, facing exactly the same direction every night. It goes without saying therefore that considerable fouling accumulates beneath the roosts. The farmer is then faced with the choice of getting rid of the pigeons or ensuring nothing is stored beneath the roosts.

The easiest means of clearing indoor feral pigeons is to go at night. All lights should be left off and all sources of light coming through windows, roofholes, etc. must be screened with sacks or whatever. The darker the roost can be made, the tighter the pigeons will sit, even to the point of being touched without flying. If they can be reached by ladder they can then be hand caught one by one without so much as a flutter. Torches can be used to good effect so long as the man keeps the light in their faces and ensures no hand comes between torch and pigeon. In effect, torches are only required briefly to make sure of a roosting bird's precise position before hand catching it in the dark.

If access to the roosts is not possible the birds must be taken by torch and rifle. Many people, pesters included, use air rifles for this job. Personally I find that CB caps – the lightest bullets available for .22 rifles (not air rifles) reduce the rifle to a power only marginally above the best air rifles. Using this ammunition the job can be done far more professionally. The object, of course, is to cleanly kill one bird for each shot without making any holes in the roof. As each target will be sitting perfectly still, even a man on his own operating both torch and rifle should be able to produce efficient results. The birds are rarely more than thirty feet from the floor and, hit in the chest cavity, will fall dead as stones and will also prevent the bullet reaching the roof. With less powerful weapons it is necessary to aim for the pigeons' heads which of course are easily missed and, even if hit, do not stop the shot.

Although night shooting of feral pigeons should provide a one bird to one shot ratio, it is a job which should never be attempted without the backup of the vermin dog; no type of shooting should. There is nothing worse for customer relations than injured pigeons hopping under nearby materials on the floor to be found next day by the staff. An experienced dog will meet each pigeon as it falls, thus preventing any such losses or indeed suffering.

Another piece of advice regarding shooting with a torch: only complete darkness stops the pigeons flying while shots are being fired. For this reason it is vital the torch is switched off at the precise moment each shot is fired. If it is left on too long there is a danger of the remaining birds, frightened by the noise, using the light to fly off. For those who normally work alone as I do, it is a good idea to tape the torch to the underside of the gun barrel in such a way that the left hand can operate the switch while maintaining a natural shooting grip. A sound moderator or silencer is, of course, a must for this job and most other uses of guns in pest control.

Cage Trapping

Cage trapping is a useful means of catching feral pigeons. A flat roof with easy access is required to site the cage. If no flat roof is available it may be possible to construct a flat platform between two sloping roofs. The cage itself must be at least 1 foot high by 3 feet by 4 feet. On all four sides of the cage are a series of 6 inch by 6 inch access holes for the pigeons. The cage is sited and baited with a large amount of maize, maple peas and wheat in the ratio 5–2–2. The amount used depends on the size of flock using the area. It should be enough to last for about a fortnight. Keep an eye on this bait at regular intervals, especially during the final days, as the pigeons must not be allowed to finish it. If the pigeons refuse to eat in the cage, it may also be necessary to bait the platform outside the access holes. The object of the exercise is to accustom the birds to feeding in the cage, so external baiting must be kept to an absolute minimum and should stop as soon as bait is being eaten inside. When all the flock has adopted the cage as their main feeding place it is time to adapt the entry holes so that the birds can get in but not out. This is done by fitting wire mesh funnels to the interior of the holes in lobster pot fashion. The interior opening of the funnels is about three inches square. Hanging wires which swing in but not out are sometimes used but are a very poor substitute for funnels. The quantity of bait is now reduced to a few handfuls. When the funnels are first fitted the cage should be emptied of captives two or three times daily to avoid overcrowding. It is always best to leave one of the captives in the cage at this stage to act as a decoy. I always choose the lightest coloured hen, as it will be seen well from a distance and will not squabble with birds which approach the cage, as some cock pigeons would do. No one feral bird should be used as a decoy for more than one day. When catches drop to three or four pigeons per day it is time to remove the funnels and revert to high quantity baiting once more. So it goes on, with alternative periods of catching and 'prebaiting'. An easy way to do it is to set the funnels Monday to Thursday and prebait over the weekend. This allows a regular weekend break from the toil of daily visits. Near the end of the pigeon trapping programme all the fearless ones will have been caught, thus leaving a small flock of shy birds. This remnant squadron has been used to following the dominant birds and is now very scatty and flighty and to an extent trap shy. The pester who does a lot of pigeon trapping will find it well worth while to acquire a white hen racing pigeon. This bird can be used as a decoy when trapping becomes difficult. Of course, a drinker and some shelter must be provided for it in the cage, as it will be confined throughout the catching periods. To fit a transparent shelter which will not frighten the ferals and which will allow the decoy to be seen at all times, construct a perspex box 10″ × 10″ × 10″ with a spar but no floor. Fix this to one of the upper corners inside the cage. It will be found that the sight of a tame pigeon feeding happily and calmly in the cage will reassure the feral birds and make trapping a lot easier.

As with all rural pest control methods, there are good and bad times to cage trap pigeons. The best time is undoubtedly when a blanket of snow covers the fields. Naturally, the trap bait should be kept clear of snow at all times. At sowing and harvest, pigeon trapping will be difficult. Also in mid-summer, when breeding is at a peak, they tend to have their minds on other things. (Whenever possible during the breeding season of any animal or bird, the control methods should not be those which only account for adults.)

Narcotising

It is quite rightly illegal to poison birds, no matter how much of a nuisance they may be. Narcotising is a licensed method of stupefying feral pigeons long enough to catch by hand. Any 'non-target' birds which take the bait will make a full recovery in a short time, especially if kept warm for a while.

As with cage trapping, it is necessary to prebait with untreated wheat or maize until the pigeon colony is feeding more or less exclusively at the bait point. By gradually reducing the daily prebait, the pigeons will feed in competition with one another. The idea is to have them racing for the bait as soon as they come off the roost at dawn. When this has been accomplished, the narcotic treated bait is set under cover of darkness just before dawn. From concealed positions the area is watched as the pigeons stir, stretch, preen and finally fly over to the bait. If all goes according to plan they will greedily squabble for their breakfast. Within minutes the first of them will be on the ground, walking around groggily or just sitting about. It is best to remain concealed so as not to disturb those still feeding. Within an hour all should be quiet and the pigeons and bait can be gathered up. Remember to check all roofs and nooks and crannies. I usually take the dog over the ground before leaving and she invariably finds one or two which have fallen among clutter or other places where they can't be seen.

There is no doubt wheat works best, but maize is less attractive to other birds. There are all sorts of recommendations about the 'humane' gassing or other destruction of the doped pigeons but most countrymen are perfectly practised at neck wringing which is quick, humane and very easy. The dead birds and unused bait should be burned to prevent any scavengers or predators eating them. I have purposely not named the narcotics used. Anyone using this method will receive all the necessary information when applying to the Ministry of Agriculture for their licence. The actual operation should be carried out with the full co-operation of the Ministry and the local vets, RSPCA, SSPCA, etc. just in case any pigeons fall outside the property.

Collared Doves

The lovely little collared dove, smooth and creamy with a delicate black collar is another newcomer to these shores. Since the early fifties when they first nested here, they have reached plague proportions in some agricultural areas. It seems their success has been helped by escapes from aviaries where they have always been popular for their soothing appearance and ease of breeding. Their UK population explosion also coincided with a period when birds of prey were extremely scarce due to the effects of agricultural field sprays.

Even in areas where they are not numerous enough to attack growing crops, their main forces will be found living wherever grain is freely available i.e. granaries, maltings, farm grain driers, distilleries, and the like. If such places have handy roosting and nesting trees close by the collared doves have all they could wish for, and their numbers will snowball. Most of what they are eating is wasted spillage so it is just the droppings, caused by sheer weight of numbers, which is a problem. Bird droppings on popular tree roosts will do no good at all to any younger trees or shrubs below and the trees themselves will eventually suffer. Rain water gutters round the roof edges will become blocked and weed seeds in the droppings will grow in these blockages, until expensive cleaning is required or repairs needed due to water seepage into buildings. Droppings falling in stored grain intended for human consumption are a real health hazard, of course.

Cage traps work well in collared dove control but, as in all types of baiting, any other food lying around must be cleared away. This is usually impossible in places where lorry loads of grain are constantly arriving, departing, tipping and spilling. For the same reasons narcotising is rarely used. Shooting is the normal control method where numbers warrant it. Rifle shooting is best at trees around maltings etc. Shotgun shooting over decoys from hides is best where wandering flocks are attacking growing cereals or vegetables in the fields. As explained in the gun/ammunition chapter, the correct choice of ammunition is vital for varying ranges/targets. Using the right combination of weapon and ammunition, it is possible to effect good control with a maximum of clean kills and a minimum of winged birds. As in all types of shooting a trained dog is vital to ensure instant retrieval and despatch of injured birds.

Starlings

Starlings come to the pester's attention at various times of year. In spring individuals often fall down chimneys while searching for nest sites. If the fireplace is not open, as is the case in many homes nowadays, the pester is often called to investigate the scratching and scraping in the wall, frequently reported as a rat. Apart from the humane necessity to open the fireplace and rescue it, there is also a purely practical reason for getting the bird out. Reports of rooms full of bluebottle flies are, as often as not, traced to some maggoty bird or rat which has died in a sealed fireplace, cavity wall etc.

Most starlings which manage to nest without falling down chimneys present no problem whatsoever. Apart from the odd tree hole, they will nest in and on our buildings. Sometimes the fouling or noise from such a nest will attract complaints, especially where they are right outside a bedroom window. What with fouling of the glass and incessant chattering very early on summer mornings, people can get upset. However the more noise comes from a nest, the older the fledglings are. A reprieve for a day or two will allow them to fly. Then the nest hole can be proofed before the parents lay another clutch of eggs. Nests in ventilation ducts and suchlike can be a problem. Nests used year after year become an amazing size and can easily block these ducts. Another problem from certain pigeon, starling and sparrow nests is the disconcerting appearance of fowl mites and other parasitic insects in the nearest rooms. The number and variety of tiny insects which can be shaken from a removed bird nest is an education. Book lice, spider beetles, mites, lice and other common insect pests often infest houses after migrating from a bird nest under the eaves into the warmth of the rooms.

Winter

It is in the winter that starlings really become a pest. Vast flocks arrive from the continent to spend the cold months here. Feeding in the fields by day they are perfectly innocent, probably beneficial. Come late afternoon however, and the scattered feeding flocks take to the air and gather into twisting swarms of thousands. As darkness approaches they descend like animated storm clouds onto their chosen roosts. Fortunately for the countryman the majority of flocks favour large industrial structures and urban roosts. Unfortunately there are always places where they will choose a forestry plantation. Night after night they crowd into the branches with only a wingspan between each bird. Night after night the droppings build up like snow on the foliage and undergrowth. Defoliation and deformation of the nursery woodland can easily be the result if action is not taken. Killing and proofing are both out of the question. Repelling or 'dispersal' is the only answer. Quite simply birds like peaceful and safe places to spend the night. By being at the roost before the swarms arrive, it is possible to keep them airborne by a combination of bangs, flashes and general hullabaloo. Some determined ones will land but some will move on. Each successive evening will see fewer and fewer starlings trying to come in. After four or five days the site will be strangely silent, the flocks having found somewhere more hospitable to spend the night.

House Sparrows

Of the three sparrows, house, tree and hedge – only two are true sparrows. The hedge sparrow is wrongly named and is just another perfectly innocent insectivorous hedgerow bird. Of the other two only the house sparrow is a pest at times, mostly because it likes houses and often because it likes grain.

Surely everyone knows the house sparrow. If you only know one sparrow this is the one you will know, a chirpy, cheery, bouncy little brown bird. We always moan about American introductions such as mink, grey squirrel and coypu. We forget how homesick settlers took British species to America. The house sparrow has taken over there just as it has here. That such a small inconsequential bird can colonise a nation the size of America, pushing native birds out of nesting sites in the process, gives some idea of its adaptability. Closely associated with man, it would be rare to find a house sparrow nest which was not in a man made structure. We provide his nest site, his food, his night roosts, everything. Probably looked upon as a town bird, the sparrow's love of grain ensures that many still live the country life. Living and nesting in farm buildings, cottages and villages they feed around cereal fields and grain stores by day. In the fields, even ripe wheat, barley or oat crops they rarely do enough damage to worry about. It is inside grain stores where they foul grain with droppings, feathers and nesting material. As many cereal eating insects are also found in bird nests there is an obvious danger of them introducing an insect infestation. Proofing can be very effective in many stores. Where constantly open doors or some such negates proofing, the pester must turn to cage trapping or narcotising.

As explained earlier both trapping and narcotising rely upon the use of bait. Where grain abounds these methods may not work, though it may be found that bread or some other attractive bait takes their attention. In the event that neither proofing, trapping or narcotising is effective, the pester has to use his ingenuity to effect a remedy. Plastic decoy hawks are available and can be run along overhead lines as if flying through the building. This throws the sparrows into a real panic. If used in conjunction with other repelling techniques this may force the birds to forsake the premises. A decoy owl, or hawk in a perching position will, on the other hand, attract sparrows, whose natural instinct is to mob such an intruder. By siting the decoy close to a makeshift hide it is possible to shoot many using .22 shot, or 'sparrowhail' as it is often called. This is a strange little ammunition, in effect a shotgun cartridge for use in a .22 rifle. Although ultrasonic devices and other repellants have been tried, it is a shame that an abundance of food means the only real answer to grain store sparrows is in their killing. One alternative is mist netting. A mist net is so fine that, when draped like a curtain over a door it is almost invisible and birds can be made to fly into it. Many sparrow jobs are made very difficult where the use of a well placed mist net would make them simple. However this method is illegal and can only be done by a pester holding the appropriate licence.

18

Squirrels

Great controversy surrounds the dark black blocks of spruce and other foreign firs which patch our upland landscapes these days. Environmental groups campaign for the increased use of native deciduous hardwoods by forestry companies. In truth, it can be practically impossible to establish young native hardwoods where the grey squirrel abounds. His predilection for eating the buds, roots, young shoots and bark of our common British broadleaves is the most important eceonomical and ecological reason for his strict control in the country setting. Sycamore and beech are great favourites of the grey squirrel, but most other hardwoods suffer also.

In the orchard he is a menace to fruit, be it unripe, ripe or over ripe. His habit of feeding on the move means much more fruit is damaged than is actually eaten. There are many other, though slightly less serious occurrences of grey squirrel damage. In the garden he will dig up bulbs, peas, beans and other seeds. Around poultry or game birds, he will steal a large percentage of the grain or other feed. Being a born acrobat, he is even able to raid the various bird feed hoppers with which farmers and gamekeepers often try to outwit him.

He is even denied the sympathy which most cuddly-looking pests are afforded by the 'animal lover' brigade. This is due to his habit of taking and eating the eggs and nestlings from every bird's nest he comes across. He has been referred to as the 'tree rat'. There is also the fact that the grey squirrel just does not belong here. He is an unwelcome American import. However well-meaning these introductions of foreign species may be, they more often than not end in disaster. In this case, the disastrous effects are mainly being borne by our own native Red squirrel, an animal of infinitely more innocent habits. The red squirrel is a shy, retiring animal of mainly coniferous woodlands. Red squirrels do not enjoy human company or open spaces. They very much prefer to keep themselves to themselves. The only time they concern the pester is when they share a habitat with grey squirrels. It is then difficult to control the greys without harming the reds. It can be done however, and it must be done, or the greys will surely multiply at the expense of the reds.

It is amazing how brash and regardless the grey squirrel can be in human

37   A double catch of grey squirrel in a 'single catch' cage.

38   Squirrel multi-catcher with double flap entry tunnel.

company. I recall a hospital, its numerous wards and departments scattered throughout expansive, grey squirrel infested grounds. One small building frequently had squirrels nesting in and pattering around the roof space. Grey squirrels in roofs are not at all unusual, but are highly dangerous due to their habit of gnawing at insulated electric wiring. In this case, they were not only causing regular fuses, blackouts and fire risks. They had even gnawed a few holes through the ceiling, allowing access down into the rooms. One chap, telling how he entered his office to find one sitting in his chair, remarked 'Things are getting bad when they replace you with a squirrel!'

Such is the boldness of this pugnacious pest, that it is little wonder he has colonised so much of the country despite continued attempts to stop him. As with all successful settlers there now seems no way to prevent the general spread of the grey. As with the urban fox, there is little harm he can do in town. But there are frequent calls for his numbers to be controlled in the many rural situations already mentioned. Control methods chosen to reduce or clear grey squirrels rather depend upon the other woodland animals present and whether they be friend or foe.

Tunnel Traps

Tunnel traps containing Fenn Mk IV's or Imbra's will account for a great many. As these traps will also control stoats and weasels they are effective on the game preserve but not on the rabbit job (where mustelids, with the exception of mink can be tolerated). Curiosity will take squirrels into tunnels, but bait can also be used. The popular bait for grey squirrel is maize. Of course, any attractant such as wheat, peanuts or raisins may be used, but maize, being yellow, seems to catch their eye. Bait for tunnel traps is not set in the tunnel but rather scattered around outside.

Where both red and grey squirrels are present, it is neccesary to choose a method which is selective only to greys. Shooting or cage trapping are the main choices.

Shooting

Shooting is best done between January and early April when the trees are bare and the disturbance is over before the woodland wildlife and game is breeding. By February the greys are already breeding and are to be found in the rather obvious dreys, especially on miserable days, which are best for drey shooting. A sectional aluminium pole giving access to fifty feet is enough for one man to prod most dreys. Another man with a shotgun and possibly another with a .22 rifle make up the team, (and as always – a dog). The men should work their way through the forestry in a systematic manner so that few dreys are missed. The essential difference between red squirrel dreys and those of the grey squirrel is that the latter's drey consists of twigs in leaf. Dreys of bare twigs belong to red squirrels and should not be disturbed.

Though drey poking by an organised team is the most productive shooting method, good results can be obtained by a lone rifleman stalking quietly with a .22. Of course, he should choose a better day for the job and will find squirrels most active for two or three hours after dawn, or in the evening.

Cage Trapping

Cage trapping or live catching is vulnerable to well-meaning interference and even vandalism where there is public access. However, it is the most popular squirrel control technique in woodland where the owner has no interest in controlling ground vermin or small predators. Multi-catch cages are best for woodland sites and will continue to catch after the first capture is made. As with all cage trapping, there is less suspicion of the cage after the first catch is inside it. Single catch cages are available for grey squirrels and are all right in garden, orchard or roofs where only individuals or small groups are causing damage.

In multicatchers the means of entry is via one or more top hinged doors at an angle of 45 degrees. These the squirrel can push in but, of course, the doors cannot be pushed out. A squirrel can, of course, pull such a door open from inside. For this reason a second angled door is often set a foot or so inside the first. Being both practical and inventive, verminmen frequently make their own cages, nets, snares etc. When making squirrel cages, it is as well to bear in mind the wire mesh must be of a size which allows reasonable light and sight into the cage so that it will look less suspicious to the squirrels. It must, however, be able to resist the nut splitting dentition of the grey squirrel and even the attentions of any fox, badger, cat or dog which might try to get at the captives.

Firstly, the cages are set on clear areas of the forest floor about 200 yards apart. The doors are tied open to allow free access and the cages and their immediate surroundings are prebaited with the maize. This is checked regularly but only the bait inside is topped up. When the bait outside is finished it is time to drop the doors to commence catching. Prebaiting normally takes four to ten days depending upon the amount of natural woodland food available to the squirrels. By coincidence, the best cage trapping time in spring and early summer is the period when rising sap, opening buds and tender shoots make young trees most attractive and susceptible to grey squirrels. Set cage traps must be checked daily but more frequent visits should be made over the first day or two of catching especially in heavily infested woods. Multicatchers can easily become overcrowded to the point of discouraging further catches until emptied. Half a dozen squirrels is a good catch in a cage two feet square by five inches high. Having filled the cage with squirrels the pester now has the problem of disposing of them. It is, of course, irresponsible to release them elsewhere in the countryside. It is also illegal to keep grey squirrels in captivity without a licence. Wild animals are not suited to a caged existance anyway. That only leaves humane destruction of the captives. (Under law 'cruelty to animals' does not normally apply to wild animals. It does, however, apply to wild animals in confinement in cage traps.) For this reason, and for plain moral decency, 'humane destruction' should mean just that. Unfortunately the numerous interested parties all make differing recommendations as to the forms this humane culling of live trapped animals should take. Advice may be sought from the RSPCA, Ministry of Agriculture, Game Conservancy, Forestry Commission, BASC, Police or other sources. Some will recommend shooting them in the cages. I have even seen the .410 shotgun suggested for this purpose. Bear in mind the cost of cage traps or the time and trouble needed to make one! In reality, the only 'guidelines' which are compulsory are those found in law. Thankfully, the legal position is far less confusing than the plethora of advice from elsewhere. The law states that any method may be used so long as it does not constitute an act of cruelty to the animal. The law is only concerned to see that the animal does not suffer unduly in the process. Thus any humane method of destruction may be used.

It is normal to have a small exit door on the cage trap. To this can be fitted a carrying box or sack before opening the cage exit and encouraging the squirrels into the carrier. The cage can then be reset and the squirrels removed in the carrier for humane destruction elsewhere.

Poisons

Poisons for grey squirrels are regulated by Law. The Grey Squirrels (Warfarin) Order 1973 gives the type of poison, the type of hopper it must be used in, and more importantly, the counties where it may be used, i.e. those areas not containing red squirrels. As the situation regarding poisoning of grey squirrels varies so much across the country I do not intend to go into great detail here. Suffice to say full information regarding all regions are available from local offices of the Ministry of Agriculture.

The law on this matter, and indeed all laws concerning wildlife and pest control, are flexible and liable to change from time to time. Although all my references to law are correct at the time of publishing I would advise the layman, customer or pester to take advice before acting upon marginal issues. The NCC, Game Conservancy, Ministry of Agriculture, BASC, Forestry Commission, RSPB and other bodies all give up to date information regarding laws, rules, recommendations and regulations. Rural pest control operations may seem very natural and far from the madding crowd, but red tape and bureaucracy abound and have to be taken account of.

19

Voles

Barking of trees and resultant damage in forestry plantations may be caused by deer, grey squirrels, hares, rabbits – and voles. Despite being diminutive in size comparison to the other bark strippers, the destruction of young trees by voles can be just as evident – often more so. This takes the form of gnawing of bark, roots and buds. In the main we are talking here of the short-tailed field vole and bank vole. Both voles are extremely abundant throughout the countryside. They are the staple diet of all our predatory animals and birds. The main difference between the species is the bank vole's climbing ability. This means bank vole damage to bark and buds can be high in a young tree or shrub while field vole barking is always at ground level. The concentrated nature of field vole barking makes it the more serious of the two pests. It is not at all unusual for field voles to completely 'ring' all nursery conifers over a small area, leaving distinct patches of brown trees in otherwise green plantations. Later these degenerate into bare clearings among the unaffected trees. Field voles are inhabitants of rank grass cover. Thus barking at the foot of trees is often hidden by rough vegetation. Field voles also burrow under young trees, especially beech and oak, to eat the roots causing the tree to lean over or fall flat.

Although vole damage is both common and serious among young trees there is little use in seeking to reduce the vole numbers. Spraying between trees with a herbicide to clear rough cover will prevent vole numbers building up in the plantation. As for all bark gnawers there are various repellent sprays, pastes, guards etc. which can be applied to the young trees.

Water Vole

The water vole is not very well known. The water rat is widely talked of. Whenever rat problems occur near burns or rivers the customer often reports the culprits as 'water rats'. Allow me to educate you; the water rat does not exist. 'Water rat' is an unfortunate folk name which people give to the water vole. There is also the problem that the common brown rat is a great swimmer and frequently found along watersides. Both animals are similar in size and colour. In truth the water vole is our largest but least harmful vole. Their burrows can be a problem in water retaining banks but any other charges against them are negligible and do not call for control. The only water vole job I ever encountered was reported as moles in a council house garden, with no running water for miles around. Even although I saw one and knew voles to be the problem I set a couple of half barrel mole traps and cleared them that way. Being rather selective eaters, all the voles are very tricky to poison but field voles and bank voles will take mouse poison in a whole or broken cereal base. Grass seed is perhaps the best.

20

Insects

Insects are killed by insecticides. Insecticides have been responsible for immeasurable harm to nature over recent years. Thankfully, farmers are beginning to realise the folly of over reliance upon chemicals. Even now the main task of insect control in the country (in standing crops) is met by farmers themselves. I would have it no other way, though I welcome the restraint many are now showing. Where the pester is involved with rural insect control is mainly in houses, gardens and indoor stores of grain and other cereals.

Following depopulation of the countryside due to agricultural advancement and the break up of larger estates, many cottages are no longer inhabited by countryfolk. Improved transport, affluence, commuting and a desire to escape the 'rat race', has brought many townfolk to live in the country. People who have been brought up in a relatively insect-free environment are often unprepared for the casual insect intruders to be found from time to time in the average rural house. Caravans, for example, are particularly attractive to earwigs. Houses with stone floors are appreciated by woodlice or 'slaters' and silverfish. In or near farm buildings flies can be a problem, even a plague! Garden ants nesting close to the house or even under the walls will begin to forage indoors in February, many weeks before it is warm enough for any to venture outside.

Because of the vast variety of insect species to be found in the woods and fields it stands to reason that the indoor insects reported to the rural pester are far more varied than those his urban counterpart may encounter. Many of these are not pest species and therefore cannot be identified by any pest controller, who is not also a naturalist. Certain large common insects in the country are of such fearsome appearance as to cause general panic whenever an individual is found indoors. These include the scorpion-like devil's coach horse beetle, the vividly orange and black striped burying beetle, the big dark and frequently mite infested dor beetle and churchyard beetle, the enormous and sinister looking wood wasp whose great long 'sting' is nothing more than a tube for depositing eggs into fissures in tree bark: the list is long and varied. Despite their alarming appearance it is enough for the pester to pick up the offending insect and release it outside: an act which is often applauded as immensely brave by the terrified onlookers!

Often it is numbers rather than appearance which terrifies people. Here we come to wasp nests and bee swarms. In some summers, following an open winter, the pester sometimes finds himself spending an entire day doing nothing other than treating wasp nests. In lawns, roofs, wall ventilators, under eaves and even in nest boxes intended for the blue tits, queen wasps are adept at finding such secure sites for establishing a colony when they emerge from hibernation in spring. Chewing old wood to produce papier maché, she builds a golf-ball sized nest in which she lays a few eggs. When these hatch she hunts for small insects on which to feed the larvae. Very soon these grubs pupate into the first 'worker' wasps of the year and take over all hunting, guarding and nursing duties, allowing the queen to get on with her job of continually churning out eggs. She never leaves the nest from that point forth. By autumn the nest can be the size of a prize pumpkin with several thousand workers coming and going. I find the whole subject fascinating, especially the internal structure of the nest. I remember once thinking I had found a sheep carcase in a loft (rustlers don't just exist in cowboy films). Closer inspection revealed the largest wasp nest I've ever come across. Considering the average wasp nest contains at least several hundred wasps and that I treat at least a hundred nests per summer, I think the fact I have only ever had four stings tells something of our unjustified fear of all wasps and bees.

Sheer panic descends with every summer swarm of bees. Bee swarms in flight can admittedly make an awesome noise and spectacle and, as they are no more than a great mass of sexy bees in hot pursuit of a single queen, they tend to alight upon the strangest places, wherever she is forced to put down for a rest. Sundials, chimney pots, garden shrubs, pillar boxes and the like are suddenly a mass of bees, hanging on to one another in clumps like animate treacle.

It has to be remembered, however, that these are domestic honey bees which have swarmed from someone's hive. Though the pester is often called he should never set about killing them with spray, powder or gas. The caring pester will have made previous arrangements with one or two local bee-keepers and will keep their daytime phone numbers handy for such eventualities. The idea is to have them uplifted as soon as possible before they move on again. Personally, I have a catching box supplied by a beekeeper. Called to a swarm I scoop them into it and drop them off at his home in return for an empty box for the next swarm (and a couple of jars of honey for myself!)

There is an even less troublesome bee, the Andrina mining bee, which as far as I know has no sting. At least I have never been able to induce one to sting me despite catching them in ungloved hands. This bee is entirely innocent but causes great concern and demands for the destruction of its colonies simply because it is almost identical to the domestic honey bee of swarming and stinging reputation. Most reasonable people on being assured of this insect's beneficial harmlessness, are quite happy to put up with its numerous tiny burrows in their gardens.

I mentioned earlier that our main reasons for destroying pests were Disease, Damage and Distress. Many insects only cause distress. I am always rather reluctant to kill an animal because the complainers don't happen to like them. Some modern people have become so alienated from nature they do not like to come in contact with it in any way. Are we to kill any species these people ask us to simply on the grounds of 'distress'?

Don't get me wrong. There are the 'Stored Product Pests' which occur in bulk grain stores. These weevils, mites and other minute but innumerable specks cause immense wastage of foodstuffs annually. Tropical insects such as the various cockroaches and foreign ants – despite an inability to thrive outdoors and a reliance upon man to transport them from one heated building to another – have managed to reach even the most isolated of rural hospitals and institutions where they present a serious health risk. Such insects causing damage and disease must be relentlessly eradicated. However, a certain amount of latitude should apply in some cases of so called 'distress'. Fortunately, the more serious the pest, the more chemical preparations are available specifically for it. There are literally dozens of sprays, powders, gels, dusts and the like available specifically for cockroaches, for example. But the cockroach is chiefly an urban pest. The casual intruders and garden insects which may invade rural properties are taken far less seriously by the pesticide producers. People all over the country who have an inaccessible and annually recurring nest of garden ants beneath their house are still waiting for a really effective cure to come on the market.

When we come to talk of cures for insect problems we return to the subject of chemical treatments. These are freely available from your local vermin-man. He has a wealth of written information at his disposal and he is in no need of any repetition of it in this book which is concerned only with the endangered skills of his trade.

Suffice to say that insects make up a fair proportion of his summer workload and any pester developing more than a passing interest in the world of insects will undoubtedly find the subject totally absorbing.

I don't expect to persuade every one to don rubber gloves, pick up a heaving mass of bees and attempt to juggle every last one into a litle wooden box. I would however hope the next customer who calls him out to a burying beetle on the curtains isn't told 'I don't know what it is but it doesn't look like any of the pest species!'

21

Near Pests and Non-Pests

If you're wondering how a whole chapter in a pest control book can concern animals which are not pests, please allow me to explain. There are, for some unfortunate reason, certain creatures which the majority of so called intelligent humans just can't stand the sight of. Spiders and bats are obvious examples. Makers of horror films seem to require liberal quantities of both in every scene.

Bats, in reality, are small harmless insectivores which do not, in fact, get tangled in your hair or suck blood from your neck. These animals which fill you with horror should, in fact, fill you with wonder. Bats are the only mammals which can truly fly. When man tried to fly he began by copying the bats. All early aircraft were strangely bat-like. Even once we were flying it took us many more years to understand the bats' use of radar, which allows them to catch flying insects in pitch darkness. Even now we look in disgust at bats. We block them out of our roofs (which they use since we denuded the land of native forests). We kill them while spraying roofs for woodworm larvae. (Among many other harmful insects, bats also eat woodworm beetles.) We kill the bat's food by spraying insecticide over woods and fields. Many insects which the sprays fail to kill will carry small traces of the chemical in their bodies. After eating many such insects, bats die from a gradual build up of the poison. You'd never believe they were a protected species, would you?

On the subject of legally protected species we come to another reason why some creatures the customer may regard as pests, must be treated as non-pests. In fairness the law does sometimes allow some exemption for particular rogue individuals of a protected species. For example, the Badgers Act (1973) and its subsequent alterations allows action to be taken against individual badgers where serious damage is being done. However, this exception to general protection is strictly controlled and it is advisable for anyone considering such action to ascertain their facts first (see final paragraph of Chapter 18).

Other protected species were once considered pests but have now become too scarce to warrant any form of control. Here I include otters, polecats, pine martens and wildcat. Indeed improved knowledge of their habits and

39 Heron.

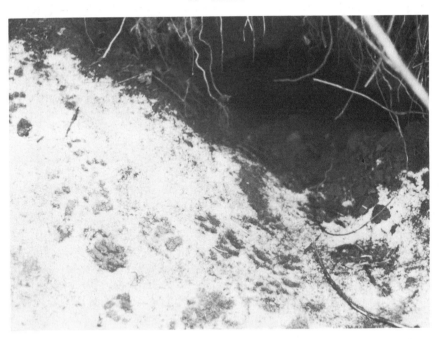

40 The occcupants of this badger set were grubbing up a sportsfield, the cure? nightly feeding with kitchen scraps!

diets have often proved them to be less guilty than was thought in the past. Even if a species is not protected it behoves us to tolerate its depredations when local or general scarcity sets in. The brown hare is a good example. From time to time the pester may be approached by pigeon fanciers being plagued by hawks, fish farmers with heron trouble or even houseproud farmers' wives with housemartin nests above the windows (and droppings on the panes). These are typical cases where either the law or the modern need for conservation must be taken into account. Here the pester must exercise a certain amount of diplomacy to ensure his refusal to act does not result in the customer taking the law into his or her own hands. A good practical naturalist should be able to come up with an acceptable answer, which is both legal and in the interests of conservation.

As repeatedly explained, a pest becomes a pest due to where, not what it is. For this reason, the caring naturalist/pester should politely try to educate the man who wants a stoat killed in a rat infested granary, a fox in a rabbit riddled plantation or a hedgehog in the garden.

Hedgehogs, though normally beneficial, can take to raiding the eggs of free range hens and even kill chicks if they catch them against wire netting etc. They are also a serious predator of partridge nests. It should be noted that spring trapping and snaring (sic) are not allowed for hedgehog control. Cage traps can still be used. Indeed hedgehogs are drawn by almost any type of bait and they are a perfect nuisance when cage traps are set for cats, rats and grey squirrels. Often the same hedgehog gets itself caught repeatedly. As explained in the insect chapter there are some large insects which look dangerous but are perfectly harmless. A knowledge of nature is all the pester requires in such cases. Indeed, be it insect, mammal, or bird the customer is often delighted to hear that this strange guest is in fact an ally which will destroy genuine pests.

It must again be realised that this book applies only to the countryside and to country people. Many animals such as the fox, grey squirrel, feral cat, and carrion crow are less of a problem in towns where there is not much livestock or wildlife for them to harm and much more of man's waste for them to scavenge upon.

So one way and another the pester encounters many reports of near pests and non-pests. As almost every British wild creature might fall into this category at one time or another, it is perhaps the animals of this chapter rather than any other which dictate the need for pesters to study nature in greater depth.

22

Future

Well, there you have it, a basic description of pest control in the British countryside of the 1980s. But what of the future? Very soon we shall find ourselves in the 21st century. How will man have changed? How will his aproach to nature have changed? How will nature herself have changed? the answers to these three questions will ultimately decide whether the craft of the country verminman survives.

Man was until recently part and parcel of nature. There is no doubt we are becoming increasingly divorced from nature, foolishly thinking we don't need her.

Lack of understanding equals fear of course. Fear of nature (or 'Distress') produces work for verminmen. There are other people it seems who, the more they lose contact with nature, the more they pay lip service to its value and talk of the need to protect it. Their only contact with nature is via television programmes which are frequently sentimentalised or humanised. It seems such people imagine wild animals live idyllic lives and eventually die peacefully of old age in their sleep. Nothing could be further from the truth, but that's how some folk think. The thought of killing animals horrifies them, and always will, until they can be made to realise that death is all part of nature. Animals live off one another. Every night of the year hundreds of them are killed and eaten by others. And yet there is no cruelty in nature. Cruelty is pain inflicted for pain's sake. Man is the only animal which indulges in cruelty. Cruelty does not occur in the natural killing of one animal by another. Nor does it apply to any countryman who is born and bred part of the natural scene and hunts for his living, as does the fox or any other predator. He has an affinity with nature. He is a participant. Nature is not cruel. Hunting is not cruel. It is all entirely natural. Unfortunately the vast majority of people now live 'unnatural', lives, and we cannot expect them to understand these basic facts.

Please don't get the idea I am against conservation. I am however, against protectionism. Protectionism is the extreme idea that no animals should be killed (tell that to the predators!). Protectionists believe good conservation is achieved simply by protecting individual animals from man. Let me say as a practical naturalist, I pray for the future of nature. Verminmen, pesters and hunters were practising conservation for thousands of years before it became a trendy fashion.

Spending my life in the countryside, I see constant destruction of nature. That destruction is caused by farmers striving to support the growing urban masses (who accuse me of being a threat to nature!). It is caused by their pollution of rivers, their acid rain, their demand for building land, and their demands for any surviving parts of the countryside to be turned into some sort of giant play park for their leisure and recreation. Make no mistake about it, the threat to our countryside, its people and the British country way of life lies entirely within our cities and within the minds of many who consider themselves 'nature lovers'!

Countrymen have been looking after the countryside for generations. I wish we could be left alone to get on with it. If a blackwinged stilt tried to nest on a British coast for the first time in years, the practical conservation methods of the countryside would include a certain amount of fox control in the area until these rare ground nesting birds became established. We would not allow the nest to be raided by foxes, and the birds frightened off for many more years, as was recently allowed to happen by some protectionists. 'Wildlife management' requires the practical skills of the verminman. Now, when we really need to do something about conservation, we would be wise to realise that fact.

There are five million field sports enthusiasts in this country at present. That includes all those who fish, shoot, hunt with hounds, fly falcons and course greyhounds. Five million is a great number. These people conserve habitat. So what if they only do it to preserve game? Their efforts preserve habitat and it is this protection of a natural environment which we need to concentrate our efforts upon. Field sportsmen, in fact, do immeasurably more good for conservation than the minority who rant about cruel sports. There are a great many woods, hedges and rough corners which would have been grubbed out, drained and 'improved' for agriculture long ago if it wasn't for their owners interest in preserving game. There are far more field sportsmen and politicians than verminmen, and the survival of the latter depends rather much upon the future of the former two. For instance, attempts by 'antis' to outlaw the use of terriers by the 'tally ho' brigade of fox hunters would, if successful, deny the use of working terriers to verminmen. Anyway, this game of political football concerning fox hunting which goes on continually between Socialists and Tories has far more to do with class prejudices than foxes. The same applies to the great socialist dream of breaking up the big country estates. If the truth be known, these estates are increasingly becoming our last reservoirs of natural habitat and thriving wildlife in a desert of decay. So what if the wildlife and habitat is conserved as a by-product of game and forestry interests? Estate owners do a damn sight more for the future of nature than any amount of antis and politicians. A proportion of the rural verminman's livelihood depends heavily upon the large country estates. And before I am accused of being a Tory, let me say that my fathers' fathers were all farm labourers.

The humane, clean, modern (and totally false) image of chemical poisons admittedly holds increasing appeal for today's customers. Rural pest control, if it is to survive this urban based competition, must embrace it and offer science as well as skill. This would give us the upper hand on those who attempt to offer science instead of skill. But my abiding hope for the future of rural pest control is that technology and tradition should combine and the small number of naturalist/pesters using both approaches should grow until the country customer can come to expect a proper service, 'from fleas to foxes'. So long as man requires pest control to continue, surely it is sensible to entrust the job to a naturalist who will place the interests of the quarry alongside those of the customer.

Though they know practically nothing of nature and the few men who remain part of it, I must concede that the future of the verminman's vocation lies with the policians and 'the masses'. Inthese unsteady hands the verminmen and his dog might easily join the long list of endangered species.

However, farming, forestry and conservation all have important futures ahead. It is my hope that practical pest control shall prosper with them.